ISAMBARD KINGDOM **BRUNEL**
RECENT WORKS

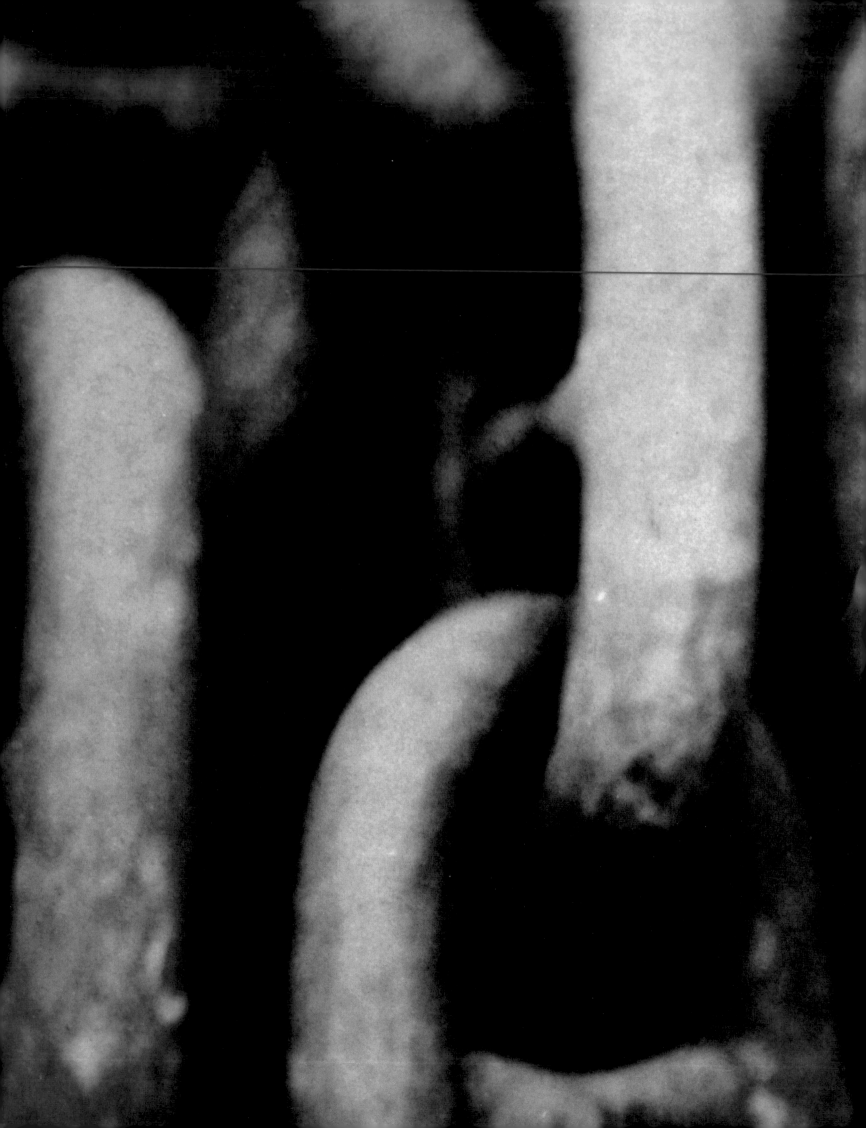

ISAMBARD KINGDOM BRUNEL

RECENT WORKS

Edited by
Eric Kentley,
Angie Hudson
and James Peto

Designed by
Isambard Thomas

This book was published to
accompany the exhibition
ISAMBARD KINGDOM BRUNEL: RECENT WORKS
at the Design Museum
from 27 October 2000 to 25 February 2001.

The exhibition was designed by
Nicholas Grimshaw & Partners
and sponsored by Railtrack.

Produced by:
Turner Libros S.A.
Rafael Calvo, 42, 2º

Printed in Spain

Published by:
Design Museum
Shad Thames
London SE1 2YD

ISBN: 1 872005 25 X

D.L.: M-40.147-2000

Isambard Kingdom Brunel stands as an iconic figure and a role model for technologists, designers, architects, engineers, artists and managers in the twenty-first century. His many qualities are as valuable today as they were 150 years ago. He had energy, talent and determination – creating visionary designs and applying new engineering principles, as well as co-ordinating and motivating people from all walks of life. He was ambitious – involving himself and inspiring others in high-risk, leading-edge projects, often of immense organisational complexity and requiring innovative solutions. He was a perfectionist, but enough of a realist to know he could not manage every aspect of his projects himself. He transformed the British landscape and changed people's lives.

David Marks and Julia Barfield,
Marks Barfield Architects, architects of the London Eye

ACKNOWLEDGEMENTS

The Design Museum gratefully acknowledges the following for lending material to the exhibition:

Elton Engineering Books

Harris (Belmont) Charity

Keith Hickman

Steve Hurst

Merseyside Maritime Museum

National Maritime Museum

National Portrait Gallery

National Railway Museum

Public Record Office

Railtrack

Science Museum

STEAM: Museum of
the Great Western Railway

The University Library, University of Bristol

The Wellcome Trust

and John Tyrell and students of the Model Making Department, University of Sunderland.

In addition to the three individuals mentioned above, the Design Museum also wishes to thank the following for their help in the organising of the exhibition and this publication:

Janet Barber

Jonathan Betts

Mike Brown

Lesley Butterworth

Diana Cashin

Julia Elton

Geoffrey Ford

Helen Forde

John Graves

Jane Holmes

Denna Jones

Hannah Lowery

Ian Nulty

Benedict O'Looney

Michael Richardson

Matt Tanner

David Wright

Ruth Wright

Special thanks are due to James Langford for his work on the design of the exhibition.

CONTRIBUTORS

ESSAYISTS

John Binding is a retired mechanical engineer and author of *Brunel's Cornish Viaducts* and *Brunel's Royal Albert Bridge*.

Tim Bryan is Curator of STEAM: Museum of the Great Western Railway, Swindon, and author of *Brunel the Great Engineer*.

Professor R. Angus Buchanan is Director of the Centre for the History of Technology, University of Bath, and author of numerous papers on Brunel, including the introduction to the Penguin edition of L.T.C. Rolt's biography.

Michael Chrimes is the Senior Librarian at the Institution of Civil Engineers.

Dr Denis Griffiths was Lecturer in Marine Engineering at the Dept. of Engineering and Technology Management, Liverpool John Moores University, and is the author of *Brunel's Great Western*.

Andrew Lambert is Professor of Naval History, Department of War Studies, King's College London ,and, with Denis Griffiths, co-edited *Brunel's Ships*.

Dr Eric Kentley is Assistant Director, Curatorial & Education Programmes, at the Design Museum.

Dr Peter Quartermaine is Senior Lecturer in the School of English, University of Exeter.

Adrian Vaughan is a railway historian and author of *Isambard Kingdom Brunel: Engineering Knight Errant*.

PROJECT ASSESSORS

Nicholas Grimshaw is perhaps best know as the architect of the Waterloo International Terminal, the redevelopment and restoration of Paddington Station and the Eden Project in Cornwall. His practice is well known for its close collaboration with engineers.

Tony Hunt is a structural engineer whose work has included Waterloo International Terminal and the West India Quay Bridge in London's docklands.

Dr John King was Tunnels Director for the UK side of the Channel Tunnel and now practises internationally as a tunnel consultant.

Vic Stephens is Director of Maunsell Rail. His projects have included the Channel Tunnel Rail Link and London Underground's Jubilee Line extension.

Fred M. Walker trained at the Clyde shipyards. He later spent twelve years as Shipbuilding Manager of the Hall Russell Shipyard in Aberdeen. He was Naval Architect to the National Maritime Museum, Greenwich, before setting up his own naval architecture business.

Jane Wernick is a structural engineer with particular experience of long span roofs and lightweight structures. Her projects have included the House of Steel, Los Angeles, and, in collaboration with Zaha Hadid, the Cincinnati Arts Center and the Bergisel, Innsbruck.

INTRODUCTION

Eric Kentley

THE CELEBRATIONS FOR the year 2000 brought three remarkable structures to London – the Millennium Dome, the Millennium Bridge and the London Eye – remarkable because the engineering component in them all has been deliberately made highly visible. Indeed, the least architectural of them, the London Eye, is proving the most popular. This phenomenon is not restricted to new buildings: the centrepiece of the reconfiguration of the National Maritime Museum in Greenwich is the largest single span roof in Europe. It is not restricted to London either – the geodesic Eden Project may yet eclipse them all. Engineering is not only back, it's bold.

Yet while the general public knows the names of the architects behind these projects – Rogers, Foster, Mather and Grimshaw – the structural engineers are anonymous. Despite engineers being as much at the cutting edge today as they were a century and a half ago, this anonymity seems to have led to a devaluation in the perception of the profession. Engineering is not seen as sexy as architecture.

It was very different in the first half of the nineteenth century when engineers were visibly creating an information super highway – the rail network. But the exhibition *Isambard Kingdom Brunel: Recent Works,* which this volume accompanies, is not a celebration of a 'golden age' of engineering, or of the life and works of I.K. Brunel. It is an attempt to explore Brunel *the designer* – how he worked, what he achieved,

and to critically examine some of his major works.

A wag once said that the Design Museum specialised in exhibitions about famous people no-one has ever heard of (*Charlotte Perriand – modernist pioneer* was our third most popular exhibition ever). But Brunel is one of those magically evocative names that everyone (at least everyone in England) knows.

To some, mention of a Brunel exhibition elicits the response 'which one?' I.K. Brunel's father, Marc, was also an engineer – perhaps even more gifted, and certainly with a more exciting biography. Born in Normandy in 1769, Marc was to study at the Royal College at Rouen under Gaspard Monge, the inventor of mechanical drawing. After six years in the French navy, he fled the Revolution to the United States (leaving his English sweetheart, Sophia Kingdom, to be interned). There he became an American citizen and, in 1796, the Chief Engineer of New York City. It was, however, his invention of machinery to produce blocks for ships' rigging that brought him to England three years later. One hundred and ten craftsmen in Southampton made 100,000 of these blocks a year by hand. Marc Brunel's machinery – the first mass-production machinery – made ten unskilled men in Portsmouth equally productive.

Marc also designed machines to produce boots, to shuffle cards, to knit, and to propel steam ships. And he designed sawmills and bridges for Russia and for Réunion in the Indian Ocean. Marc also ensured that Isambard received an

education as good as his own, sending him to Caen College and then to the Lycée Henri Quatre in Paris. He arranged for Isambard to stay with the well-known family of horologists, the Breguets, during his time in Paris.

Without Marc's influence, Isambard may never have been able to enter the competition to design a bridge at Clifton; without his father's experimental bridge at Rotherhithe, Isambard may never have been inspired to create the awesomely shallow arches on the Maidenhead Bridge. However, it worked both ways – without Isambard, Marc's most lasting project, the Thames Tunnel, might never have been completed.

Nevertheless, although Isambard may not have been as mechanically gifted as his father, he was much more prolific as a civil engineer. Not everything he attempted was successful. For example: his design for a dome for the Great Exhibition was rejected; his locomotive designs were poor; and he spent years working with Marc on a differential engine that never worked properly. But such failures are insignificant compared to the successes. He built 25 railway lines; five suspension bridges; 125 other bridges; eight pier and dock systems; three major ships; was a pioneer of operational research; and engaged in innumerable other projects – including an observatory, a rifle, water towers and a hospital.

The sheer quantity of Isambard's output makes it impossible to present a comprehensive exhibition of his work. *Isambard Kingdom Brunel: Recent Works*

presents a detailed study of just six main projects, but attempts to portray them in sufficient depth to enable the visitor to understand the challenges to which he rose. It is a relatively easy task to decide to include one bridge, one station, one ship and so on. It is more challenging to decide exactly *which*.

Both the Clifton Suspension Bridge and the Maidenhead Bridge are, in quite separate ways, staggeringly impressive structures but, as John Binding's essay shows, the Royal Albert Bridge was a masterpiece on a different level. Of the numerous stations, Paddington is the only one still surviving in use, largely unchanged after 150 years. Paddington is also an example of how Brunel could collaborate successfully with other professionals. The story of the building of the *Great Eastern* shows that his collaborations were not always happy affairs. Although the *Great Britain* (now preserved at Bristol), was one of the most significant ships of the nineteenth century, the sheer scale of the *Great Eastern*, its problematic launch, and the fact that it was effectively Brunel's last project, made its selection inevitable.

Whatever its shortcomings, the *Great Eastern* steamship is a good illustration of how Brunel adapted and developed existing technologies to create a ship unlike any other ever seen before. The issue of developing a gauge – the broad gauge – shows Brunel's ability to take a problem right back to basics. The hospital he designed for Renkioi is included in the selection to highlight his ability to produce radical and successful

solutions for problems with which he had no obvious previous experience.

However, it was undoubtedly the training that Marc provided – the combination of the theoretical formal education and the practical 'apprenticeship', as well as his own natural talent – which gave Isambard the confidence to tackle whatever challenges were put in front of him head-on. Therefore, the selection also includes the largest project they worked on together – the Thames Tunnel.

As Angus Buchanan's chapter demonstrates, Isambard was undoubtedly a workaholic and a demanding employer. But what is viewed by one commentator as arrogance, is seen by another as shyness. The aim of the exhibition and this book is not to portray Brunel's character, but his works. It is his works that are the legacy.

Henry Maudslay's model of Marc Brunel's 1802 machine for cutting mortises in blocks. *National Maritime Museum 3007*

1 WORKING FOR THE CHIEF
THE DESIGN TEAM AND OFFICE STAFF OF I.K.BRUNEL

R. Angus Buchanan

WORKING FOR THE CHIEF

BRUNEL FLOURISHED IN THE mid-nineteenth century when the railways were making their world-transforming impact and steam ships were being introduced into ocean service – and he was intimately associated with both developments. Brunel masterminded the conception, construction and equipment of the Great Western Railway, one of the major rail routes out of London, as well as its network of secondary railways. He also supervised the design and construction of three outstandingly innovative steam ships: the *Great Western, Great Britain,* and *Great Eastern*, which together profoundly changed the pattern of oceanic travel.

Along the way, he designed some ingenious bridges in iron, brick, masonry and wood; he improved the construction of dock works in various parts of the country; and he supervised and gave advice on water works, drainage schemes and a host of other engineering operations.

In the space of thirty years – from his submission for the competition to design the Clifton Bridge in 1829, to his premature death in 1859, aged fifty-three – Brunel's dynamic mind and colossal energy made him, unquestionably, one of the dominant influences in British engineering.

Even with his tremendous capacity for hyper-activity, however, he could not have achieved all he did without the support of a considerable team of assistants. To assess the significance of this remarkable man, one needs to have a clear view of

the extent and nature of his team. How did Brunel assemble his assistants? How did he organise and command them; and above all, how did they help him to design and fulfil his many projects?

When Brunel entered the Clifton Bridge competition in 1829 he was only twenty-three, but he had already served for five years on his father's staff. For most of that time he had occupied the important and responsible post of Resident Engineer on the Thames Tunnel, the great project which Marc Brunel had undertaken to drive under the river from Rotherhithe to Wapping. This operation had begun in 1825 and went on for eighteen years, but, in 1828, after battling against stupendous difficulties, work was abandoned for several years when the tunnel was overwhelmed by disastrous flooding. In the course of this inundation, the young Isambard sustained severe internal injuries and almost lost his life. It was while recuperating from this incident in Bristol, that he was first drawn into the possibilities of work there.

With the help of his father, who had experience of suspension structures and a superb eye for good engineering design, Brunel submitted a series of beautiful sketches for the Clifton Bridge competition; which, after considerable discussion and changes of mind on the part of the promoters, he eventually won in March 1831.

In the course of these negotiations, he established the links with a network of Bristol merchants and industrialists which led to him becoming engineer both to the Bristol Docks Company and, in 1833, to

the enterprise which became the Great Western Railway. Though Bristol was Brunel's base for his railway works and his first two steam ships, he did not make his home there. Instead, at the end of 1835, he acquired a large house in Westminster, 18 Duke Street, subsequently adding No. 17 next door to his property.

It was here that he proceeded to set up the substantial office from which he directed his rapidly growing engineering business. He married in 1836, and he and his family occupied the upper floors of the property (where his office appears to have been), while the business was conducted downstairs.

Brunel had previously had an office at 53 Parliament Street where, as he said, 'I have made my fortune or at least laid the foundation of it'. However, he does not appear to have had any staff there, and the first appointments for which he was responsible were of field workers. The Clifton Bridge Company had settled with him to receive 5 per cent of the cost of erection of the bridge, ie £2,500, plus personal expenses of £500, plus £800 for the appointment of a Resident Engineer and £400 for a Resident Assistant.

It is not certain how this agreement was fulfilled, but it is clear that the Resident Engineer appointed was C.E. Gainsford. With the Great Western Railway, Brunel inherited as his Assistant Surveyor, W.H. Townsend, who had been his only rival for the post of Chief Engineer, but he quickly took a dislike to Townsend's lax time-keeping and the latter soon disappeared from the records of the Railway. It seems likely that the build-up of Brunel's staff did not begin until his move to Duke Street. There, his first appointment was that of a Chief Clerk, Joseph Bennett, who joined him in 1836 and remained in office until 1859.

Unfortunately, not much is known about Bennett, although he was probably responsible for the series of fifteen Private Letter Books and the volumes covering the Railways and the *Great Eastern* which survive in the Brunel Collection at Bristol University Library. The handwriting is not all the same, as presumably, Assistant Clerks copied many of the letters, but it is reasonable to suppose that some of it is Bennett's work. He presided over the clerical work of the office and dealt with many of the financial transactions. Brunel occasionally left him to deal with routine correspondence himself and Bennett appears to have given complete satisfaction to his Chief. But as a Chief Clerk he was not required to deal with any design or engineering matters.

Amongst the first people to whom Brunel turned for engineering assistance were colleagues who had worked with him on the Thames Tunnel. These included Richard Beamish, his fellow Resident Engineer on the Tunnel, who also later acted as Resident Engineer for Brunel on the Gloucester & Dean Railway in 1845–50. William Gravatt, who had been Assistant Engineer on the Tunnel, and shared in some of the terrifying experiences there, was appointed as Resident Engineer on the Bristol & Exeter Railway. Michael Lane and Thomas Page, both of whom had worked on the Tunnel, found later employment on the Railway

works, with Lane becoming Chief Engineer of the Great Western Railway from 1860 to 1866.

The original Great Western Railway construction works were conducted in two sections: a western division, building eastwards from Bristol to Bath and on to Box; and an eastern division, building westwards from London to Reading, Swindon and Chippenham. The link between the two section, the Box Tunnel, was the biggest engineering problem on the route, and was the last part to be completed. The western division was supervised by three Resident Engineers; G.E. Frere, George T. Clark, and T.E. Marsh; and the eastern division by T.A. Bertram, John W. Hammond, and Robert P. Brereton. The Assistant Engineer responsible for the Box Tunnel was W. Glennie.

These were all very competent engineers and applied themselves diligently to their assignments (even though Marsh discovered a Roman villa on the line at Newton St. Loe and caused a slight delay by being distracted into archaeology). Clark went on to become a wealthy iron master in South Wales and Marsh built up a busy practice in Bath and Bristol when he left Brunel's service. Bertram went on to become Chief Engineer to the GWR for a year, 1859–60, between Brunel and Lane. Hammond and Brereton both became, in succession, Chief Assistant to Brunel himself – Hammond from 1836 until his death in 1847, and Brereton from 1847 to 1859.

Brereton is said to have lost an eye in an explosion while working on a station

on the eastern division, and in the portrait which survives of him, is depicted wearing an eye-patch. He was put in charge of the Royal Albert Bridge over the Tamar, at Saltash, and after Brunel's death, Brereton attended to the completion of his outstanding commitments. By arrangement with Brunel's family, he continued to practise his engineering consultancy from the office in Duke Street.

For all their competence, their Chief rarely entrusted these men with any basic design work. Brunel was not a good delegator. He liked to be fully responsible for all the work he undertook, and it was only the physical impossibility of doing everything himself, that obliged him to depend on others to be his eyes and his hands when he could not be present. His team, in short, were there to do what he told them to do and were not expected to exercise any engineering initiative.

As for design initiative, this was jealously reserved for Brunel – who had strong ideas about the design of everything he tackled. His method seems to have been to do a series of rough sketches of the rail lay-outs, the stations, the tunnels, the signals and the whole apparatus of a major trunk railway, and then to pass his sketchbooks to draughtsmen in his office to be transcribed into engineering drawings.

Some of the surviving drawings for GWR structures bear his signature, but it seems unlikely that Brunel would have done the detailed work on them. Many of them are beautifully tinted and can be considered genuine works of art which he

Paxton's Crystal Palace, photographed in 1852 after the Great Exhibition had closed and before it was re-erected in Sydenham.
Victoria & Albert Museum

would not have had time to create himself. For Brunel, the creation was the Railway itself; and engineers and draughtsmen alike had the responsibility of reproducing his vision.

This was not the best recipe for a genuinely happy design team. Though most of Brunel's assistants were immensely loyal and spoke warmly of their Chief, their attitude was frequently conditioned by awe and their desire to correctly interpret Brunel's wishes, rather than by close personal affection. There were some exceptions to this pattern, one of the most interesting of which, was the case of William Gravatt.

Gravatt was the same age as Brunel, the son of an Inspector of the Royal Military Academy at Woolwich and himself a competent mathematician and Fellow of the Royal Society. He had been engaged to make the preliminary survey for the line from Bristol to Exeter, which

he had done with admirable skill and efficiency. He had gone on to supervise the construction and appeared to enjoy the confidence of the directors. But then things began to go wrong between him and Brunel, culminating in a very strong letter to Gravatt in July 1840. It began 'My Dear Gravatt', but, in the copy at least, the words 'My Dear' are ostentatiously crossed out and the letter goes on:

It appears that you entertain views and opinions differing very much from my own on important engineering questions which have been discussed and which have been settled as following part of the plan of construction of the Bristol & Exeter Railway. In this there might be nothing extraordinary but that connected as we have been as intimate friends of long standing, acting as my assistant in this course for 4 or 5 years, constantly at my side when these subjects have been discussed in public or at the board, that you should never have hinted to me that you differed and that I should hear of it now for the first time and indirectly is extraordinary ... Is this the conduct of a friend, of a gentleman, of a subaltern trusted and confided in by the man above him?

The issue was not resolved, and the next year there was another row when Brunel wrote to Gravatt regarding 'the deplorable state' of the Bristol & Exeter Bridge near the Bristol terminus and asking him to resign. His assistant, however, refused to go quietly and made counter-charges which the Board decided to investigate – much to Brunel's annoyance.

The incident may have contributed to the souring of relationships between Brunel and the Bristol & Exeter directors, who were still anxious to maintain their technical independence of the Great Western Railway, because shortly afterwards he withdrew as Engineer to the Railway.

It is frustrating that there is no other source of information about the dispute besides the letters leaving Brunel's office. The closest we get to an account of the point at issue is when Brunel observes

Brunel's dome – the rejected entry for the Great Exhibition, June 1850.
Illustrated London News

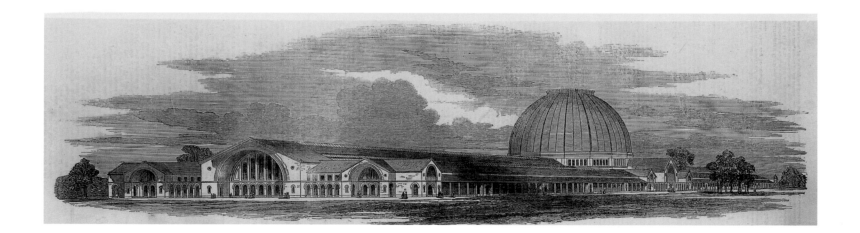

that: 'All the bridges [on the Bristol & Exeter] are built much lower than the standard long-since fixed for the Great Western.'

We know that Gravatt had his own views about bridge construction, favouring a very low angle in the arch. We know also that Brunel had trouble with at least one such bridge, over the Parrett at Bridgwater, for which Gravatt was almost certainly responsible, and which had to be totally replaced. It seems very likely, therefore, that Gravatt had committed the cardinal offence against Brunel – modifying design details stipulated by the Chief. It was an offence for which past intimacies provided no excuse as far as Brunel was concerned and marked the end of the relationship.

There were, however, some subjects on which Brunel acknowledged that he needed to take design advice – albeit grudgingly. The most important instance of this was in regard to steam locomotives.

Whatever his skills as a civil engineer, marine engineer, and engineering polymath, Brunel had his blind spots, and one of these was locomotive steam engines. By general consent, the engines that he designed and had delivered to the GWR, when it began to operate its first public services in 1838, were not capable of doing the work expected of them. Brunel was rescued from the huge embarrassment which this failure would have caused, by Daniel Gooch, the young man he had recently appointed to run the locomotive department of the GWR. Gooch first acquired excellent locomotives

from Robert Stephenson and had them adapted to the broad gauge system. Then he went on to design an outstanding series of locomotives, which virtually equipped the GWR with serviceable engines for the remainder of its broad gauge days. Brunel wisely recognised his own limitations in this area and let Gooch get on with the job in his own way, supporting him in commissioning the GWR Workshops at Swindon and appointing assistants (such as the talented Archibald Sturrock) who were responsible to Gooch.

In effect, he passed over the locomotive design and construction team to Gooch's authority. Though Brunel did not do this with a completely good grace, he remained on friendly terms with Gooch, and the latter paid him a most handsome tribute when Brunel died.

Another area in which Brunel recognised his own inadequacies and turned to his assistants for more than routine help was in mathematical skills, especially as these impinged on understanding the strength of materials and the behaviour of ships in the sea. As far as the latter was concerned, he was lucky to have the services of William Froude as an Assistant Engineer and Resident Engineer on several stretches of West Country railway. Froude was the son of an eminent clergyman and came from a talented family: one of his brothers became a respected theologian and another a famous historian. William, however, excelled as a mathematician, especially in the application of mathematical theory to ship construction,

and as such he became a valuable guide to Brunel, when the latter was wrestling with the many problems created by the design of the SS *Great Eastern*.

Not that Brunel always accepted such guidance willingly:

I deny altogether the very foundation of your theory now that you lay it bare – the rate of expansion will not be infinite in the case you assume ... I feel I may be altogether writing nonsense – one sadly loses the habits of mathematical reasoning – The subject is one of great importance to me just at present and I should like you to pursue it.

This was in 1847, so it seems that the prospect of a 'Great Ship' was already stirring in his mind. Froude subsequently advised Brunel on the laws of the motion of ships in connection with that project, by which time he had embarked on the innovation of using testing tanks for ship designs – a technique for which he became widely known and respected.

William Bell was another assistant who was employed for several years – specifically to make calculations and experiments. Brunel had advertised a post for 'superintendence of mechanical constructions' in 1846, and when Bell applied for it, Brunel wrote to one of his referees: 'Is he industrious and intelligent and secondly is he a willing man or one of those who fancy themselves not sufficiently appreciated – of the latter class I have always a great dread.'

The reply must have been favourable, because Bell got the job and was plied by Brunel with calculations on riveting, testing cylinders under stress, and other matters which collectively made a valuable contribution to Brunel's technical grasp of the possibilities of using wrought iron girders in large structures. Bell subsequently conducted complicated mathematical calculations in conjunction with Froude for the *Great Eastern*, and contributed the chapters on bridges and dock works to Isambard's biography of his father. As with Froude, Brunel valued the mathematical skills of Bell, but it does not seem likely that he participated in any sort of design team for the *Great Eastern*.

There are at least two instances in which Brunel deferred to architectural expertise, although he generally preferred to design his own buildings, which he did with some panache and in a remarkable diversity of styles. These are the cases of the Crystal Palace and Paddington Station. The Crystal Palace, of course, was Joseph Paxton's masterpiece and Brunel had no part in its original design. However, when the Crystal Palace was removed to Sydenham, Paxton invited him to design the twin water towers, which were features of the new structure.

Brunel had served on the Buildings Committee of the 1851 Exhibition Commission, and in this capacity he had been responsible for preparing a design which came close to being accepted. This design has generally been dismissed as too heavy and massive in contrast with Paxton's elegant structure, but it did feature a striking iron dome which would not have disgraced the Exhibition.

In the event, Brunel reacted cautiously when Paxton's scheme was first mooted, and wrote to him: 'I mean to try and win with our plan, [ie the iron dome] but I have thought it right to give your beautiful plan all the advantages it is susceptible of.' But

he soon conceded defeat and became an enthusiastic supporter of Paxton's brilliant conception of a giant iron and glass conservatory became available. The iron dome, to which Brunel had given a lot of attention in the early months of 1850, was quietly forgotten.

Brunel was undoubtedly greatly influenced by the Crystal Palace when he came to design the great train shed at Paddington. He employed an architect, Matthew (later Sir Matthew) Digby Wyatt, to attend to the detailing, but the overall conception was Brunel's. [see Chapter 4 on Paddington Station]

It might not seem a happy arrangement to invite an architect to do the details of Brunel's own building, but Wyatt accepted and the resulting station stands as a monument to their design collaboration. As far as Paddington Station's hotel frontage was concerned, Brunel lost interest and left this entirely to an architect: in this case P.C. Hardwick.

There is no doubt that Brunel was a hard taskmaster. He expected his assistants to work hard and to follow his instructions. If they failed to do so he did not hesitate to reprimand them or dismiss them and the Private Letter Books record many such judgements. As early as January 1836, he dismissed G. Harrison, saying 'I do not consider that you discharge efficiently the duties of Assistant Engineer'. But he did give the man chance to redeem himself with a month's trial under Frere at the Bristol end of the GWR line.

Then in 1841 Brunel wrote to a staff member's grandparent explaining that,

'A short time back after repeated warnings to your grandson I was compelled to dismiss him from the Company's service as his excessive idleness not only rendered him useless but infected others.'

And yet he rebuked another Assistant Engineer, R.M. Marchant, for being over-bearing towards a subordinate: 'When a man complains of want of courtesy he should himself be most gentlemanly and courteous in his language which you are very far from being in your note to me.'

The curious feature about this exchange is that Marchant was a relative of Brunel, being the son of one his mother's sisters. But Brunel does not appear to have shown him any special favour on this account. Indeed, when Marchant moved off to become a railway contractor – a move that was not unusual for engineers in the 1840s – he became Brunel's adversary in the strange affair known as the 'Battle of Mickleton Tunnel' in July 1851.

During the digging of the tunnel, Marchant, who was owed £34,000, stopped work. Brunel raised an army of 2,000 navvies to force him to quit the site. On this occasion, Brunel demonstrated that he knew his man – because when confronted with such determination, Marchant capitulated. His business subsequently collapsed and he wrote to Brunel complaining that it was his fault, but Marchant received short shrift: 'As long as you wish to abuse me you must have the goodness to do so in some other way than by writing to me as I shall return your letters unread.'

The implication of this altercation is not necessarily that Brunel was right and Marchant was wrong. Brunel drove his contractors like everybody else under his orders; and in some cases he could be unreasonable in his demands – as in the notorious instance of his refusal to pay the contractor McIntosh the money to which he was entitled for his work between Bristol and Bath. This developed into a long-standing legal dispute, which only ended long after the deaths of both McIntosh and Brunel, when it was ruled that the GWR was obliged to recompense the family of the contractor. The incident serves to illustrate an attitude towards subordinates on Brunel's part which was over-forceful, and even, on some occasions, arrogant. It also demonstrates the extent to which he ran his large business as a one-man-band as far as planning and decision-making were concerned. As far as his railway works are concerned, there is little indication in Brunel's relations with his subordinates of anything resembling a design team. Nobody but the Chief was allowed a role of independent significance.

The situation was slightly different with regard to the three ships designed by Brunel. In every case the original conception appears to have been his, and his sketchbooks contain many drawings showing outlines and general arrangements of the vessels. But for the detailed design work he seems to have accepted the need to call upon the expertise of more experienced ship builders. In the case of the SS *Great Western* this meant the Bristol ship builder

William Patterson, in whose shipyard the ship was constructed, with some help from the Admiralty. Whether or not a formal design team was ever assembled is not clear, but it is certain that there were many separate consultations for advice in the course of construction, and that Brunel accepted this advice.

With the SS *Great Britain,* the situation was changed by the fact that she could not be accommodated in any existing Bristol shipyard, so the Great Western Steamship Company was obliged to secure its own shipyard and extend an existing dock for the construction of the vessel. This was undertaken, furthermore, not by practising ship builders but by a workforce assembled by Thomas Guppy and Christopher Claxton. Both these men were close colleagues of Brunel in the Company and had been closely involved in the first ship project. Guppy was a Bristol entrepreneur with an engineering business, and Claxton a retired naval officer and Bristol Docks Quay Warden. Brunel got on well with both of them and made great use of their skills; so it could be argued that the three of them comprised an effective design team for the *Great Britain* – the first large iron ship and also the first such ship to be screw-propelled.

The task of this team was further complicated when Maudslay, Sons & Field (the distinguished London firm that had provided the steam engines of the *Great Western*) were reluctant to tender for the engines of its successor, which were projected as being substantially larger. The task of designing the new engines

devolved eventually on Brunel himself, and, by drawing on an arrangement patented by his father fifteen years earlier, he was able to produce an ingenious and effective set of engines.

These were made on-site in Bristol, under the supervision of Guppy when Brunel was not present himself. Guppy was nine years older than Brunel, but the two appear to have worked well together. There are copies of around fifty letters from Brunel to Guppy in the Bristol Collection and they come as near as anything in the collection to being a design consultation. Brunel writes about details of the engines in a letter covered with small calculations:

Have had a very long talk with Field … and am glad to say that my views are fully born out … after an hour's discussion I think I satisfied him that we had all been going on the wrong tack and I think that the speed of the engine has nothing to do with the speed of the boat – it is only the pressure exerted by the piston at the end of the piston arm.

Subsequent letters deal with fittings and equipment, design problems and screw-testing. The lengthy discussion of such technicalities suggests a close working partnership, and at one point in the correspondence Guppy appears to have suggested a formal arrangement on these lines, because Brunel answers evasively, 'relatif to you and I working together', but does not pursue the matter. Whatever the formal nature of the relationship, the two men were of like mind and became close friends, and when Guppy was obliged to move his business to Naples for reasons of health, Brunel lost the close support of one of his best advisers.

Another view of the
Duke Street Office,
c. 1859.
Elton Engineering Books

THE DESIGN TEAM AND OFFICE STAFF OF I.K.BRUNEL

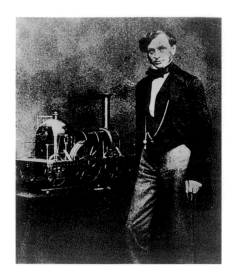

Daniel Gooch, locomotive designer, aged 29. The model in the background is in the collection of the National Railway Museum. *Science Museum*

By the time the project which was to become the SS *Great Eastern* began to mature in the early 1850s, Guppy had departed and Brunel's other close friend, Robert Stephenson, did not get into marine engineering, so Brunel was thrown back on his own resources. He attempted to provide himself with the expertise he required in large iron ship construction by entering into a vaguely defined partnership with John Scott Russell; but this later proved to be a disaster.

Russell certainly had the required expertise, but his way of working accorded with old ship building traditions and was profoundly frustrating for Brunel. There was some basic discussion of design, but never a happy design team, as Brunel found himself having to supervise many details of construction in order to ensure that his wishes were carried out. The wonder is that the enormous project was carried through at all, and the fact that it was completed successfully (from a technical point of view) is a tribute to Brunel's enormous capacity for hard work and mastery of detail.

He had able assistants on the job, such as the Resident Engineers William Jacomb, Henry Wakefield, and the young Bradford (later, Sir Bradford) Leslie, who joined him as a pupil in 1847 and was then used by Brunel to monitor the work being done by suppliers of equipment for the Great Ship. Despite all the support he received from many competent assistants, the construction of the *Great Eastern* was essentially a one-man virtuoso performance rather than a team effort.

There are signs that Brunel's office staff was declining towards the end of the 1850s, as his railway commitments diminished and the *Great Eastern* consumed so much of his time and energy. It is not possible to calculate the size of this staff with as much precision as is desirable, because no general wage book has been found, and although there is an abundance of bankbook stubs and partial accounts there is no way of being sure that everybody who deserves to be included has in fact been accounted for. But it seems likely that in its prime, during the 1840s, the office would have consisted of about thirty people, including Assistant and Resident Engineers, draughtsmen, clerks and pupils.

We can identify several pupils amongst the names available, although Brunel protested that he could not cope with them and insisted he could devote no time to them. This did not prevent a constant flow of applications (some from directors of companies and others to whom Brunel might have owed a favour) asking for places for their sons or relatives. Brunel reduced the pressure on himself by putting up his costs. In 1836 he charged 600 guineas, but by 1846 his charges had risen to £1,000:

That is to say £550 on entering and £150 a year for three years – and one year for nothing making in all four years during which time I profess to take no trouble whatsoever with the youth – he has all the opportunities which my office of course give him – and if he turns out well gets employed in responsible situations which improve him.

It seems unlikely that there were ever more than one or two such pupils in the office at any one time.

There was one moment in the life of Brunel's office when a circular letter is recorded as having been sent to all members of the staff, the list coming to a total of 33 names. This was in 1850, and the occasion was a notice inviting designs for a competition in connection with preparations for the Great Exhibition. It cannot, however, be assumed that all of the listed men were currently in full-time employment with Brunel.

Beamish, for instance, had probably completed his commission on the Gloucester & Dean Forest Railway, and by 1850 Babbage would have been preparing to emigrate to Australia. Also, the numbers could have been reduced by the downturn in the railway boom, as the previous year Brunel had written to one of his staff:

These are very economical times. I foresee an extreme probability of the GWR Directors calling upon me to make an almost clean sweep of all expenses on the Wilts & Somerset no body must rely upon employment after this quarter.

On the other hand, J. B. Hannaford, and five other members of the drawing office staff who do not appear on the list, were dismissed shortly after the notice was circulated. So the estimate of a total staff of about thirty at any one time when Brunel was in mid-career is almost certainly of the right order of magnitude. Those who appear in the 1850 lists are marked with a '+' in Table on page 25, which sets out the names of most of those who are known to have served with Brunel in these years, about whom some information is available. It provides

a useful guide to the number, quality and variety of the team.

Another indication of the complexity of Brunel's office arrangements is the fact that it took his Chief Clerk, Bennett, several months to wind up operations after the death of the Chief in September 1859. On 20 September he wrote to the Metropolitan Life Assurance Company: 'Sir – I am desired by the Executors of the late Mr. Brunel to inform you that his death took place last Thursday night the 15th Inst.'

Bennett then notified sixteen Secretaries of Railway Companies of the death of their Engineer, together with five senior members of staff and sixteen Assistant Engineers.

Bennett was particularly anxious to register Brunel's claim as 'Inspecting Engineer of the Government of Victoria', which amounted to £2,063, so on behalf of the Executors of Brunel, he sought an assurance from the Duke of Newcastle (the Secretary of State for the Colonies) that an arrangement would be made for the completion of the other Australian contracts outstanding with the office. He suggested appointing Brereton, who, he stated:

… has been upwards of 23 years in Mr.Brunel's service, and for some time past has been chief of his Engineering Staff and he has under Mr.Brunel had charge of the former contracts for the Victorian Railways.

It seems likely that Daniel Gooch had turned down a request from Bennett to remain 'the paid professional adviser' on matters referred to the office by the Victorian Railways in Melbourne.

Brereton also took over engineering responsibility for the West Somerset Railway. At the end of December, Bennett wrote terminations of responsibility notices to eight of the senior members of staff, including Samuel Jones, T.E. Marsh, William Bell, P.J. Margary and Charles Richardson. It is likely that some of these were re-appointed by their respective companies because Richardson, at least, continued to supervise the engineering works on the Bristol & South Wales Railway, going on to become one of the promoters of the Severn Tunnel and a major entrepreneur in South Gloucestershire. This was the same Richardson who had once been reprimanded by Brunel for giving too much attention to cricket, although he had then used the possibility of cricket to lure him into the Bristol & South Wales Railway project :

William Froude, engineer and naval architect.
Science Museum

THE DESIGN TEAM AND OFFICE STAFF OF I.K.BRUNEL

The Tunnel referred to here was that at Patchway, north of Bristol.

One of Bennett's last jobs was to acknowledge contributions towards the memorial for Brunel. He wrote to thank William Fairbairn for subscribing twenty guineas in December, and later in the month he responded to a letter from Wellington Purdon, acting for Brunel on the East Bengal Railway, who had written in great concern when the sad news had reached him. Bennett thanked him for his sentiments: 'The public feeling has been great and it is to be more thoroughly demonstrated by a memorial, what the character of it may be has not yet been decided upon.'

Bennett continued to wind up the business as neatly as he could and in March he decided that the time had come to depart. His last letter was dated 30 March 1860, and with that the main series of entries in the Private Letter Books terminated.

Brunel did not like to be described as a 'consultant engineer' because he felt that 'consultation' was too remote from responsibility. He preferred a full hands-on commitment to any project which he undertook, and he expected to be in full charge as 'Engineer in Chief'. The enormous engineering business which he developed, however, resembled in all important particulars the type of 'consulting engineering' practice as first established by John Smeaton in the eighteenth century, and subsequently adopted by Telford, Rennie, and the other great names of the British engineering profession.

The only difference was one of emphasis on the absolute responsibility of the Chief, as no decision of any substance went through his office without his specific authorisation. He initiated all design work; monitored all drawings; kept a close eye on all fieldwork and construction; and approved all financial transactions with contractors, suppliers and staff.

The only exceptions in this rigorous process of supervision appear to have been those undertakings which were too far afield to be subject to close inspection, such as Brunel's overseas commitments in Italy, India and Australia.

Even here – and especially in the case of the Italian Railways in the 1840s – he required frequent and regular reports from his agents in the field and kept them supplied with a stream of instructions.

Also, there are some indications of a weakening of the supervisory procedures towards the end of Brunel's career, when he was preoccupied with the problems of the *Great Eastern* and his physical powers were declining.

But for the most part (and certainly for the most creative period of his professional life, from the mid–1830s to the mid–1850s) Brunel ran a 'tight ship', where to question his absolute authority would have been to invite dismissal. He may have been a benevolent autocrat – but he was an autocrat all the same.

Brunel was not only Captain of his team but he was also in charge of virtually all other operations as well. It says much for the breadth of intellect, and the amazing capacity for prolonged hard work of the man, that he was able to carry this off. But it did mean that his 'team' was incapable of operating efficiently without the constant presence of its leader.

Any consideration of Brunel's 'design team' must therefore acknowledge the personal quality and commitment of the Chief himself. His personality was always larger than life. His staff mainly regarded him with loyalty, and even affection, but these sentiments were based on a sense of awe at the super-human powers of their Chief. Brunel viewed his team as an extension of himself, and it enabled him to do much more than he could have done without its assistance.

But, ultimately, the team had no existence except as part of Brunel's personal activity, and without his presence it immediately lost its vitality. Many of Brunel's assistants went on to distinguished engineering careers themselves – Gooch, Froude, Leslie and others – but none of them replicated the scale of Brunel's operations, or the intensely personal control which he was able to exercise. Brunel's 'team' was unique in British engineering history for the significance of its highly personalised structure.

THE ENGINEERING TEAM OF I.K.BRUNEL

* = PICE obit;

+ = 1850 List;

RE = Resident Engineer;

AE = Assistant Engineer;

P = Pupil

12/43 = December 1843, reference to Private Letter Books;

35–42 = 1835–42;

£ = pounds sterling]

	Name	Dates	Details
+	BABBAGE, Benjamin Herschel	1815–1878	RE, Italian Rlys 42–48; S.Australia
	BAGE, Edward	....	AE, Taff V.Rly (12/43)
+*	BALY, Price Richard	1819 – 1875	P, Hungerford Br. (5/50); Europe
+*	BEAMISH, Richard, FRS	1798 – 1873	RE, Thames Tun; Glos & Dean 45–50
+*	BELL, William	1818 – 1892	AE, calculations (5/49); S.Devon Rly
	BENNETT, Joseph	....	Chief Clerk 36–59
+	BERTRAM, T.A.	....	RE, GWR; Chief Engineer 59–60
+*	BLACKWELL, Thomas Evans	1819 – 1863	K & A Canal; RE, Bristol Docks(12/51)
	BRATTON, T.	....	AE, Oxford W& W Rly (1/52)
	BRERETON, Robert P.	....	RE, GWR; Chief Assistant 47–59
+	BRODIE, R.	....	AE, GWR; RE, S.Wales Rly (2/52)
*	BRUNTON, John	1812 – 1899	AE, Cornwall (1/52); RE, Renkioi (2/55)
	BUSH, H.S.	d.by 1843	AE, Taff V.Rly (12/43)
	CLARK, George T.	....	AE, GWR 35–37; Dowlais Iron
	CLARK, Seymour	....	First Traffic Supt., GWR
	COFFIN, W.	....	RE, Taff V.Rly (1/43 and 7/43)
+*	EDWARDS, Osborne C.	1822 – 1876	AE,Glos &Dean 45–50;Cork [Freemason]
*	ENGLAND, John	1822 – 1877	AE (1/42); offered N Devon Rly
	FRERE, G.E.	....	RE, GWR(W.Div);(1/46) [Archaeology]
*	FROUDE, William, FRS	1810 – 1879	RE, N.Devon Rly; ship calculations
	GAINSFORD, C.E.	....	RE, Clifton Br; O&B Rly; Tamar Br.
	GANDELL, J.H.	....	AE, GWR (misappropriation 3/40–11/40)
+	GLENNIE, W.	....	AE, Box Tun (3/36); Tamar Br (3&11/55)
	GOOCH, (Sir) Daniel	1816 – 1889	GWR, Chief Loco.Eng, Swindon (10/40)
*	GRAVATT, William, FRS	1806 – 1866	AE, Thames Tun; RE, B&E Rly 35–42
	HAMMOND, John W.	d. 1847	RE, GWR (E.Div);Chief Assistant 36–47
	HARRISON, G	....	AE, GWR (dismissed 1/36)
	HERRING, Walter	....	AE, GWR (Bath, 2/44)
	JACOMB, William	1832 – 1887	RE, ssGE 55–59
	JAMES, John	....	AE, O&Rugby Rly (1/46: £300 + house)
	JOHNSON, W.	....	Surveyor, GWR(Stroud); Italy (7/42)
+*	LANE, Michael	1802 – 1868	AE,Thames Tun; GWR,Chief Eng.60–66
	LESLIE, (Sir) Bradford	1830 – 1926	P, 47; AE, ssGE 56–57; India
	MARCHANT, R.M.	....	AE,GWR?; contractor, Mickleton Tun,51
+*	MARGARY, Peter John	1820 – 1896	AE, B&E Rly; RE,S.Devon and Cornwall
*	MARSH, Thomas Edward M.	1818 – 1907	RE, GWR Bath 41; WS&W Rly 46–
*	MOORSOM, Capt. William S.	1804 – 1863	Sandhurst; Lickey; Cornish Rly (12/44)
+	OWEN, W.G.	....	AE, GWR (1/36 @ £150)
*	PAGE, Thomas	1803 – 1877	RE, Thames Tun; London (offer 7/45)
+*	POWER, Samuel	1814 – 1871	USA 34–37; RE, Plymouth Docks 47–57
*	PURDON, Wellington A.	1815 – 1889	Woodhead Tun; RE, Wexford; E.Bengal
+*	RICHARDSON, Charles L.	1814 – 1896	RE, Hereford R&G;Bris.&S.Wales 58–
	STURROCK, Archibald	1816 – 1909	Works Eng., Swindon 40–50; to GNR
	TOWNSEND, W.H.	....	Bris & Glos Rly; 1st AE, GWR and B&E
*	WAKEFIELD, Henry	1823?– 1899	P, GwssCo(notice 6/55); AE,ssGE
+*	WARD, Richard James	1817 – 1881	AE, GWR (reprimanded 10/44)
	WILD, C.H.	....	Gt.Exhib. (5/50); Crystal Palace (10/53)
	WYATT, Sir Matthew Digby	1820 – 1877	Architect, Paddington (1/51 and 12/57)

2 THE ENGINEERING OF THE THAMES TUNNEL

Mike Chrimes

Section through the
tunnelling shield.
Science Museum

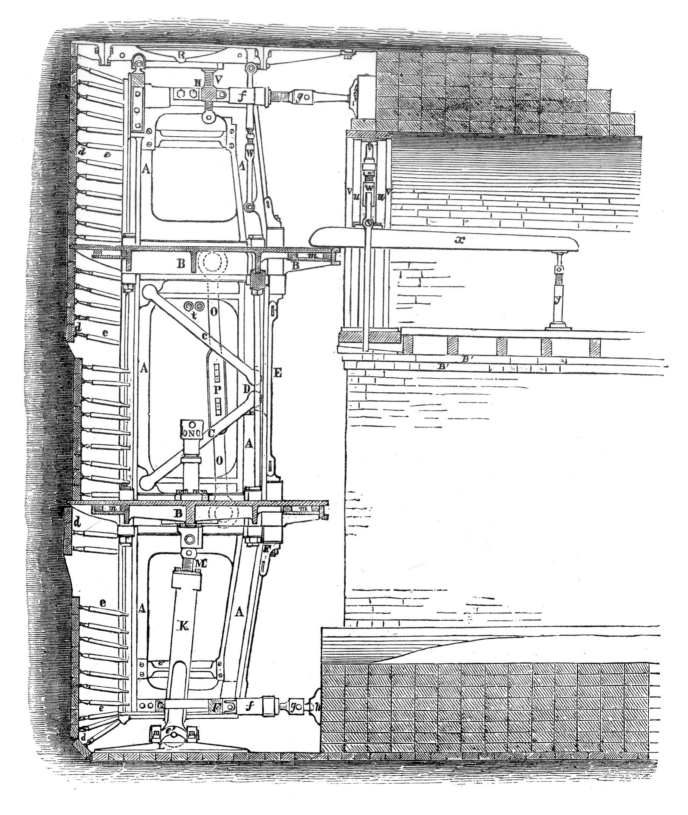

THE ENGINEERING OF THE THAMES TUNNEL

THE THAMES TUNNEL, designed by Marc Isambard Brunel, has long been acknowledged as one of the landmark civil engineering structures in the British Isles. It was recognised as such by the Institution of Civil Engineers' second President, James Walker, as long ago as 1847, when he wrote:

I have often said and thought that it is the greatest engineering work in this country, on account of its final success after so many accidents, and the means that were taken to overcome them.

More recently, in 1993, the American Society of Civil Engineers, jointly with the Institute of Civil Engineers, affixed a plaque denoting it an 'international civil engineering landmark'.

Its engineering significance is manifold – the first modern sub-aqueous transport tunnel in the world and the first use of a tunnelling shield in soft ground. Either would qualify it for landmark status. But it is the problems which Marc and Isambard Brunel had to overcome, which have captured the imagination of modern commentators as much as their contemporaries, and given it a greater significance than an engineering 'first'.

As well as the Tunnel itself, Marc designed the tunnelling shield and supervised the works from inception to completion. The challenge of designing a truly prototypical structure was complicated by the immense geo-technical problems which threatened to halt construction. These difficulties were compounded by financial problems and further aggravated by a poor working relationship between Marc Brunel and the Chairman of the Tunnel Company.

The extraordinary achievement of the Tunnel features in many contemporary published accounts, as well as more modern histories of the Brunels. It even became the focus of a specialist society. And the recent commemoration of the 150th anniversary of the Tunnel opening has inspired a critical re-examination of contemporary source material.

The published results of these studies have proved timely (in the light of London Underground's decision to carry out works on the Tunnel) as they have served to re-emphasise the structure's historical importance. These papers have also helped clarify uncertainties over the construction and engineering geology of the Tunnel.

What then were Marc Brunel's problems and what engineering solutions did he adopt?

The Thames Tunnel is a brick structure, 1,202ft long, built between 1825 and 1843, joining Rotherhithe and Wapping beneath the Thames in East London.

By the time of the commencement of the Tunnel in the early 1820s, mining techniques were well advanced and permitted the construction of deep shafts and galleries – such as those beneath the sea off Cornwall and under the River Tyne.

These tunnels relied heavily on the development of steam engines to keep the workings dry, and generally made use of pit props to support narrow drifts through rock. Later, the canal age provided an opportunity for civil engineers to build on this experience, developing tunnelling techniques for a variety of transport projects.

Sir Marc Isambard Brunel
by Samuel Drummond,
c.1835.
National Portrait Gallery

29

The diving bell used by
I.K. Brunel, May 1827,
Clarkson Stanfield.
*Guildhall Library,
Corporation of London*

Thames Tunnel shaft
under construction,
Carl Friedrich Trautmann,
c.1835.
*Guildhall Library,
Corporation of London*

Canal tunnels (generally brick lined) had been built which were over three miles in length. The geological problems encountered in their construction had already revealed this to be one of the most difficult branches of civil engineering. It was an area where some of the earliest specialist contractors were to emerge.

An alternative area of expertise was the military tradition of the Sappers, and their use of timbering in soft ground was familiar to Marc Brunel.

By the end of the eighteenth century, confidence in tunnelling techniques was such that schemes were proposed to tunnel under major rivers like the Firth, Tyne, Mersey and Thames. In the case of the Thames, work began on two schemes: one at Gravesend, where a shaft was sunk between 1800 and 1802; and the Thames Archway project, launched in 1804. This scheme reached within 70 feet of the north bank before ground conditions and lack of funds led to its abandonment.

Marc Brunel would have followed these developments with interest. In 1812 he himself gained practical experience of tunnelling in soft ground in Chatham Dockyard.

Around 1816, his observations of the way the shipworm, *teredo navalis,* bored through timber, led him to the idea of a tunnelling shield as a means of supporting an excavation in soft ground.

In 1818, he took out his patent for tunnelling shields – his earliest ideas bearing a striking resemblance to more modern circular tunnelling shields – more so than his final designs for the Thames Tunnel shield.

As Marc developed his thinking, he began to promote the idea of a tunnel east of London Bridge, in docklands, where a bridge was ruled out by navigation interests. He eventually settled on the Wapping-Rotherhithe alignment.

From the problems encountered during the Thames Archway experience, Brunel was keenly aware of the treacherous ground conditions which might be encountered. He had, therefore, to design a shield capable of supporting both the face of the excavation and the area around the shield whilst it was advanced, but before the permanent, brick, lining had been installed behind.

Brunel's problems were magnified by the scale of the cross-section of the Tunnel – 38ft × 22ft 6in – which remains one of the largest tunnel sections ever driven in soft ground.

Brunel abandoned the original circular form of the shield and replaced it with a rectangular form which he felt would give better support to the ground. In its final form it comprised 36 cast iron cells in a dozen frames, which were capable of being jacked forward against the brickwork lining independently of each other. Brunel arranged for some site investigations before work began.

Unfortunately, the boring tools used produced misleading information, suggesting a layer of impervious clay continuous across the river, and of sufficient thickness to protect the roof of the Tunnel from inundations from the Thames. Brunel was concerned that if he drove his Tunnel too deep he would hit water-bearing strata (still the tunneller's

THE ENGINEERING OF THE THAMES TUNNEL

nightmare) and felt he had identified a geological condition through which the Tunnel could safely be driven.

Work began in 1825, with the sinking of brick-lined shafts at Rotherhithe using methods developed in the sinking of wells. Tunnelling began in December and problems were immediately revealed in co-ordinating the advance of the shield.

Throughout the period of construction, problems were experienced in maintaining the Tunnel's alignment and preventing damaging distortion of the frames. As the workforce gained experience, progress was relatively rapid. Marc, however, remained concerned about the ground conditions. Isambard carried out further investigations in 1826 which, although more reliable, failed to give any indication of the problems which were to follow. As tunnelling proceeded, there was an inevitable destabilising of the ground around the Tunnel. Had there been a continuous bed of clay of adequate thickness above the Tunnel, the consequences would not have been disastrous; but the clay proved perilously thin and became softer as work progressed.

These problems were made worse by the layers of sand and silt encountered which flowed into the excavations when exposed – all serving to undermine the overlying strata which protected the Tunnel from the river.

Progress became slower, and in May 1827 there was a major flooding of the works, which had now reached 554ft. An enormous hole in the riverbed had to be plugged with 2,500 tons of clay-filled bags and gravel. Although work continued, money was now running out and, in January 1828, when there was a second major irruption in which sixteen men lost their lives, work had to be suspended. Eventually, the Tunnel was completed with the help of a Treasury loan. While the financial problems were sorted out, Marc worked on the development of a slightly larger, improved shield. When work recommenced in 1835, his first task was to develop a means of supporting the outlined excavation around the existing shield in order to enable it to be removed and replaced by a larger structure.

The design and execution of these temporary works was another outstanding piece of civil engineering, involving an early application of 'soil nailing' to stabilise the ground. Tunnelling restarted in 1836, and although early progress was satisfactory, by December 1836 conditions were worsening, with increasingly frequent runs of sand (as much as 28 cubic yards a day in February 1837). Throughout the whole of 1837 the tunnel progressed by only 29ft. There were major irruptions in August and November, and again, in March 1838.

Marc had to develop a different method of working, jacking forward the timber piling boards at the face of the Tunnel against the soft ground. This, combined with constant depositing of clay bags on the riverbed and the placing of clay pockets to improve the ground around the shield, finally made the completion of the Tunnel possible in December 1841.

Much emphasis has been placed on the engineering and construction of the Tunnel, but it must also be remembered that – perhaps uniquely up to that time for a transport tunnel – Marc was also concerned with the architectural finishing, inside and at the entrance to the Tunnel, which would be seen by those passing through it. Completion of these design features meant the Tunnel was not opened until 1843.

Despite recent research, uncertainties remain about the engineering of the tunnel. Although Marc's detailed investigative approach is well documented, recent controversy has revealed a lack of knowledge of just how much he knew about the strength of contemporary brickwork and mortar.

For those who have visited the tunnel recently, the exposure of the drainage system raises the question of just how it was designed; how it was intended to work and, even, when it was installed – during construction or after completion? Furthermore, the full implications of co-ordinating the daily advance of a multi-cell shield in, at times, appalling geological conditions during construction of the Tunnel, are not fully known.

What is recorded, is the extraordinary reaction to the Tunnel when it was opened on 25th March 1842. Within twenty seven hours 50,000 people had paid to pass through its turnstiles. Queen Victoria asked for a personal tour and within fifteen weeks the Thames Tunnel was already receiving its one millionth visitor.

F 5 10 15 20 25 30 100 200 300 400 500

6 3 0 6 12 18

2 3

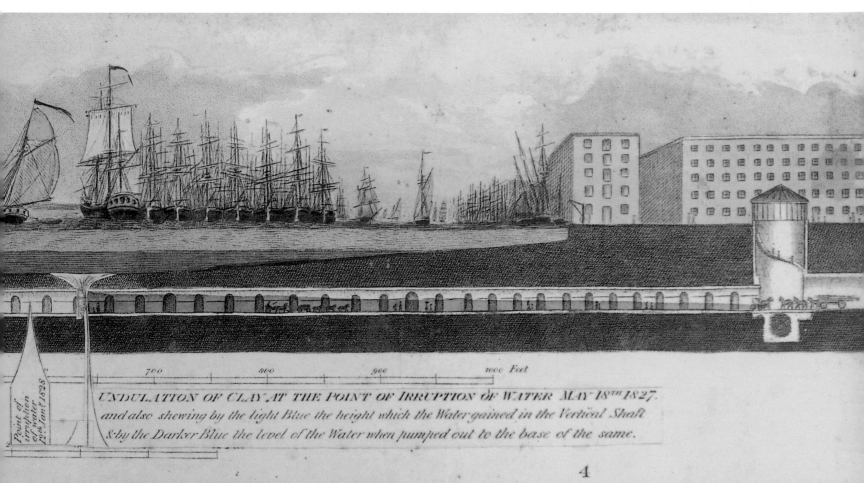

700   800   900   1000 Feet

UNDULATION OF CLAY AT THE POINT OF IRRUPTION OF WATER MAY 18TH 1827.
and also shewing by the light Blue the height which the Water gained in the Vertical Shaft
& by the Darker Blue the level of the Water when pumped out to the base of the same.

Point of
irruption
of water
12th Jany 1828

4

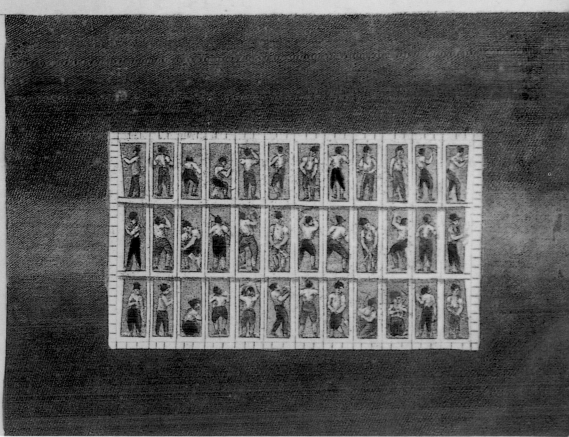

THE IMPACT OF THE BRUNELS' THAMES TUNNEL

John King

Tunnels through rock require little or no temporary support and may not even require a permanent lining at all. Tunnels in 'soft' ground, however, may require temporary support of the face and also to the exposed periphery of the excavation until a tunnel lining can be installed. Special measures are required when excavating through silt, sand and gravel; all of which can be extremely unstable when charged with water.

Modern methods of tunnelling either utilise injected chemicals to solidify (stabilise) gravels and sands, or use tunnel-boring machines which retain the ground in position with balancing hydraulic pressures, whilst the front of the machine rotates and shaves away the ground. Sometimes compressed air is used to hold back the water and stabilise the ground during excavation.

But at the beginning of the nineteenth century, when London badly needed a road tunnel under the Thames to the east of London Bridge, no-one had mastered driving a tunnel under water in unstable ground. It was known that a thick band of London clay existed there. But, above the clay, lay water-bearing gravels to the river bed – below it were equally treacherous sands under artesian water pressure.

So, in 1818, Marc Brunel patented a cylindrical tunnelling shield (see drawing) with six compartments at the front, where tunnel miners could excavate the ground, and a circular 'tail' at the rear in which cast iron segments could be assembled to form the lining. Each compartment, or cell, at the front, could be moved forward independently as the miner advanced the face using wooden board or 'polings' to secure the ground against collapse. When all the compartments had been advanced, the rear of the cylinder was to be moved forward by screw or hydraulic jacks thrusting off the completed lining and leaving room for the next ring to be assembled within the protection of the tail. The shield for the Thames Tunnel was the development from a cylindrical shield to rectangular one.

By any standards the Thames Tunnel was a remarkable feat of engineering and it provided the method by which many road, rail, sewer and other tunnels would be constructed to this day. From that time, British engineers led the world for over a hundred years in the construction of tunnels.

Whilst excavation in modern shields is carried out using a variety of mechanical methods, the principles involved – moving the cylinder forward as the excavation proceeds and holding the face and periphery of the excavation firmly in place by advancing the shield with hydraulic jacks, whilst a supporting segmental lining is added behind – are all based on Brunel's original patent.

Tunnellers, and indeed all those that need and use tunnels in their daily lives, owe an immense debt to Marc Brunel for his vision, determination and incredible fortitude.

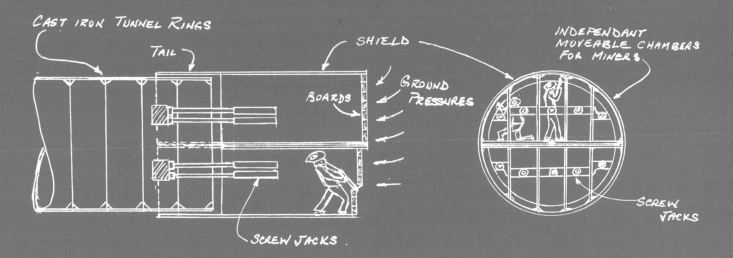

CAST IRON TUNNEL RINGS

TAIL

SHIELD

BOARDS

GROUND PRESSURES

INDEPENDANT MOVEABLE CHAMBERS FOR MINERS

SCREW JACKS

SCREW JACKS.

Marc Brunel's patented tunnelling shield (1818)

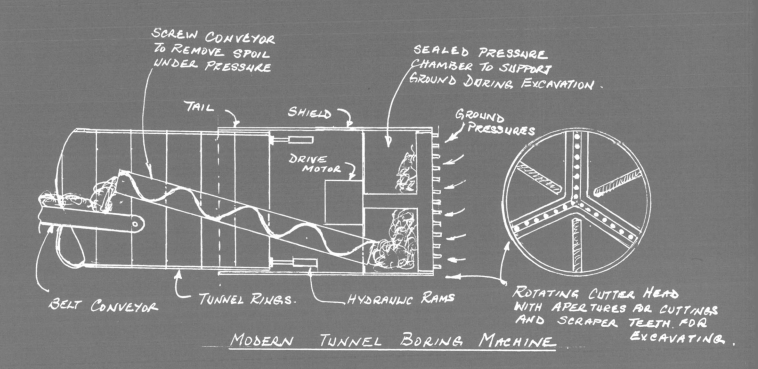

SCREW CONVEYOR TO REMOVE SPOIL UNDER PRESSURE

SEALED PRESSURE CHAMBER TO SUPPORT GROUND DURING EXCAVATION.

TAIL

SHIELD

DRIVE MOTOR

GROUND PRESSURES

BELT CONVEYOR

TUNNEL RINGS.

HYDRAULIC RAMS

ROTATING CUTTER HEAD WITH APERTURES FOR CUTTINGS AND SCRAPER TEETH. FOR EXCAVATING.

MODERN TUNNEL BORING MACHINE

Modern tunnel boring machine

3 THE BATTLE OF THE GAUGES
BRUNEL'S BROAD GAUGE

Tim Bryan

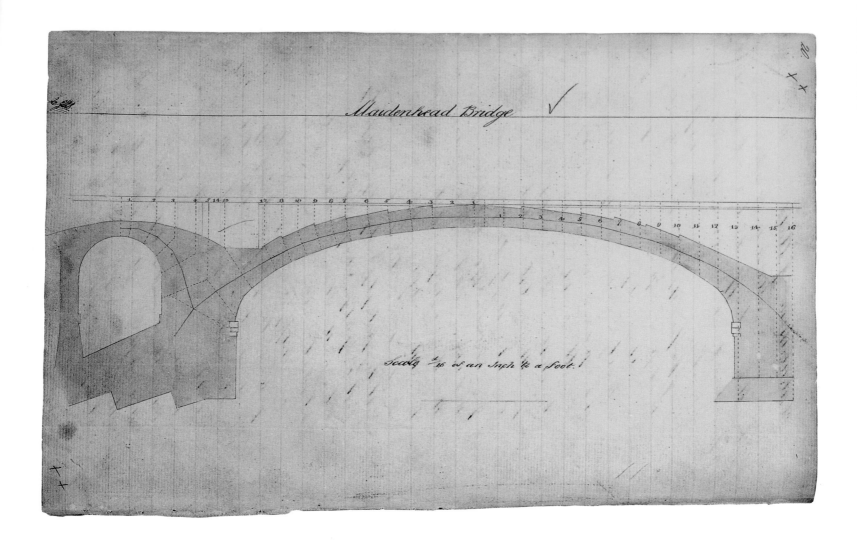

Arch analysis of the
Maidenhead Bridge in
Brunel's notebook.
The two arches were the
flattest and largest ever
built in brick.
Public Record Office

ISAMBARD KINGDOM BRUNEL called the Great Western Railway 'The finest work in England.' From the start it was apparent that this railway was to be no mere carbon copy of those already in existence.

With railway development still in its infancy, his new line incorporated more than its fair share of innovations, not least the fact that the track gauge adopted was seven feet – what became known as the 'Broad Gauge.'

Introduced in 1835, the broad gauge dominated the early history of the Great Western Railway and by 1845 had become a national issue, when the whole question of a uniform gauge for railways in Britain was debated by parliament. This contest became known as 'The Battle of the Gauges', as railway engineers and companies were ranged against each other in a debate not really settled until the last broad gauge trains ran in 1892, and Brunel's bold innovation was finally abolished.

When Isambard Kingdom Brunel was appointed as the engineer to the Great Western Railway in March 1833 he had yet to prove his worth. Nevertheless, as described in Chapter 1, he had already successfully submitted designs for the Clifton Bridge. And the reputation the young engineer had gained during his brief stay in Bristol was enough to give him an opportunity to work on another local project – that of a railway to link the city with London.

The business community in Bristol saw a railway linking their city with the capital as sound business sense. Although turnpike roads had improved, both they, and the more modern canals, were slow and expensive.

On 21 January 1833, a meeting was held to discuss 'the expediency of promoting the formation of a Railroad from Bristol to London.' With the support of important commercial institutions in the city (including the Corporation, the Chamber of Commerce, the Society of Merchant Venturers and the Dock Company), it was agreed that the first step was to undertake a survey of a route for the new railway.

Nicholas Roch, a member of the Bristol Docks committee, was asked to select an engineer for this purpose. Roch already knew Brunel well, having worked with him on a scheme of improvements to the City Docks.

Brunel was not, however, assured of the position of engineer. He was in competition with a number of other engineers who had already been involved with railway schemes in the Bristol area, including Brunton and Price, the promoters of an earlier abortive railway scheme. A more significant rival was W.H. Townsend, the engineer of the Bristol and Gloucestershire Railway, the first railway to enter the city.

Initially the brief given to each of the engineers was a simple one. The method of selection would be determined by each surveying a route, with the lowest estimate winning the job. Characteristically, Brunel responded by arguing that this process was unacceptable. He would survey the best route not the cheapest. Writing to the committee he noted that, 'You are holding out a premium to the man who makes you the most flattering promises.'

This strategy was not without its risks, and with little experience in railway building, Brunel gambled on the reputation he had gained in Bristol on the Clifton Bridge and Dock works. The gamble paid off and he was appointed engineer to the new railway, although his appointment was approved by a margin of only one vote – too close a call, perhaps, even for Brunel.

Once appointed, it was his job to survey and plan the route of the new line, a task which took several months to complete and for which he was paid the princely sum of £500. Much of the work was done by Brunel himself – riding the length and breadth of the proposed route.

With the publication of the company's first prospectus in 1834, the engineer then set about formulating his designs for the railway. However, it took two attempts to get the Great Western Railway Act through parliament, and so Brunel had time to consider the form his new line should take in some detail.

Apart from the usual concerns about costs, the directors of the company appear to have had little influence on the eventual design of the railway. What is clear is that Brunel contemplated a railway unlike any other currently in existence or being built.

The new railway featured many innovations, and Brunel's numerous sketchbooks are full of ideas for all aspects of the operation of the railway – from

Previous spread: Bristol – the meeting of the broad and standard gauges – 1870. The Great Western station is on the right; the Bristol & Exeter station is on the left. The large building contained the Bristol & Exeter Railway offices. *Public Record Office*

trackwork to bridges; from stations down to the details of the lamp posts.

Throughout the construction of the railway, Brunel was to maintain this attention to detail, trusting little to his assistants, who found him a hard taskmaster. It is not surprising that the heavy workload which came with such an approach eventually affected his health, as witnessed by his collapse from nervous exhaustion after the opening of the railway in 1841.

Despite all the preparatory work done by Brunel in the period leading up to the passing of the Great Western Railway Bill, he had said very little about the track gauge to be adopted on his new railway.

Some inkling of the changes he had in mind could, however, be gleaned from the fact that, early in 1835, Brunel was able successfully to persuade Lord Shaftesbury, (who was Chairman of Committees in the House of Lords), to omit the customary clause in the forthcoming Great Western Bill which defined the gauge of the railway.

Up until this point, the matter of track gauge had been of little consequence to railway engineers. What eventually became known as the 'standard gauge' (4ft 8½in) had its origins in one of the types of transport eclipsed by the railways – the horse.

One apocryphal story is that the wheels of Roman chariots were normally set about five feet apart. Whether this is true or not, it is more commonly agreed that most horse-drawn vehicles in more modern times had their wheels set this distance apart. Many of the horse-drawn railways or tram roads serving collieries in the North East of England had a gauge of around five feet.

It is thought that when George Stephenson was employed to build the Stockton and Darlington Railway (which opened in 1825) he chose a track gauge of 4ft 8in – not because of any particular engineering theory – but for the more pragmatic reason that Killingworth Colliery, where he had built his first steam locomotive, also utilised a track gauge of the same dimensions.

It is not recorded why the later, additional half inch was added, but the 'standard' gauge became a standard when Stephenson chose it as the gauge for the Liverpool and Manchester Railway, which opened in 1830. The Grand Junction and London & Birmingham Railways followed suit, as did other railways connecting with them.

The somewhat haphazard reasoning behind the adoption of the standard gauge on railways elsewhere, must have been one of the factors considered by Brunel when he revealed his ideas on the gauge to be adopted for the Great Western Railway, in a report to the directors in September 1835.

This report, he noted, was necessary to explain, 'the grounds upon which I have recommended to you a deviation from the dimensions adopted in the railways hitherto constructed.' Brunel argued that his new railway would be a high-speed line, with gentle gradients and curves, which would help reduce the friction between rail and wheels.

THE BATTLE OF THE GAUGES

Overleaf:
Broad gauge locomotives of the Great Western Railway Company. *Science Museum*

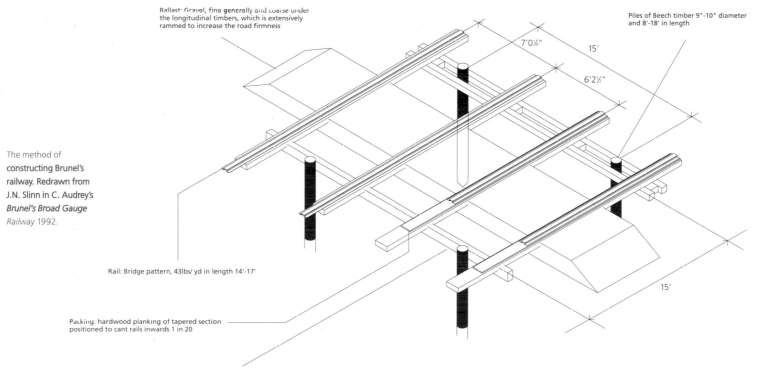

Ballast: Gravel, fine generally and coarse under the longitudinal timbers, which is extensively rammed to increase the road firmness

Piles of Beech timber 9"-10" diameter and 8'-18' in length

7'0¼"

15'

6'2½"

The method of **constructing Brunel's railway. Redrawn from J.N. Slinn in C. Audrey's** *Brunel's Broad Gauge Railway* 1992.

Rail: Bridge pattern, 43lbs/ yd in length 14'-17'

15'

Packing: hardwood planking of tapered section positioned to cant rails inwards 1 in 20

Framing timbers: American pine
Longitudinal sections 12"-14" x 5"-7" length 30"
Transom sections individual member 6"x9" deep
double members 6" square

41

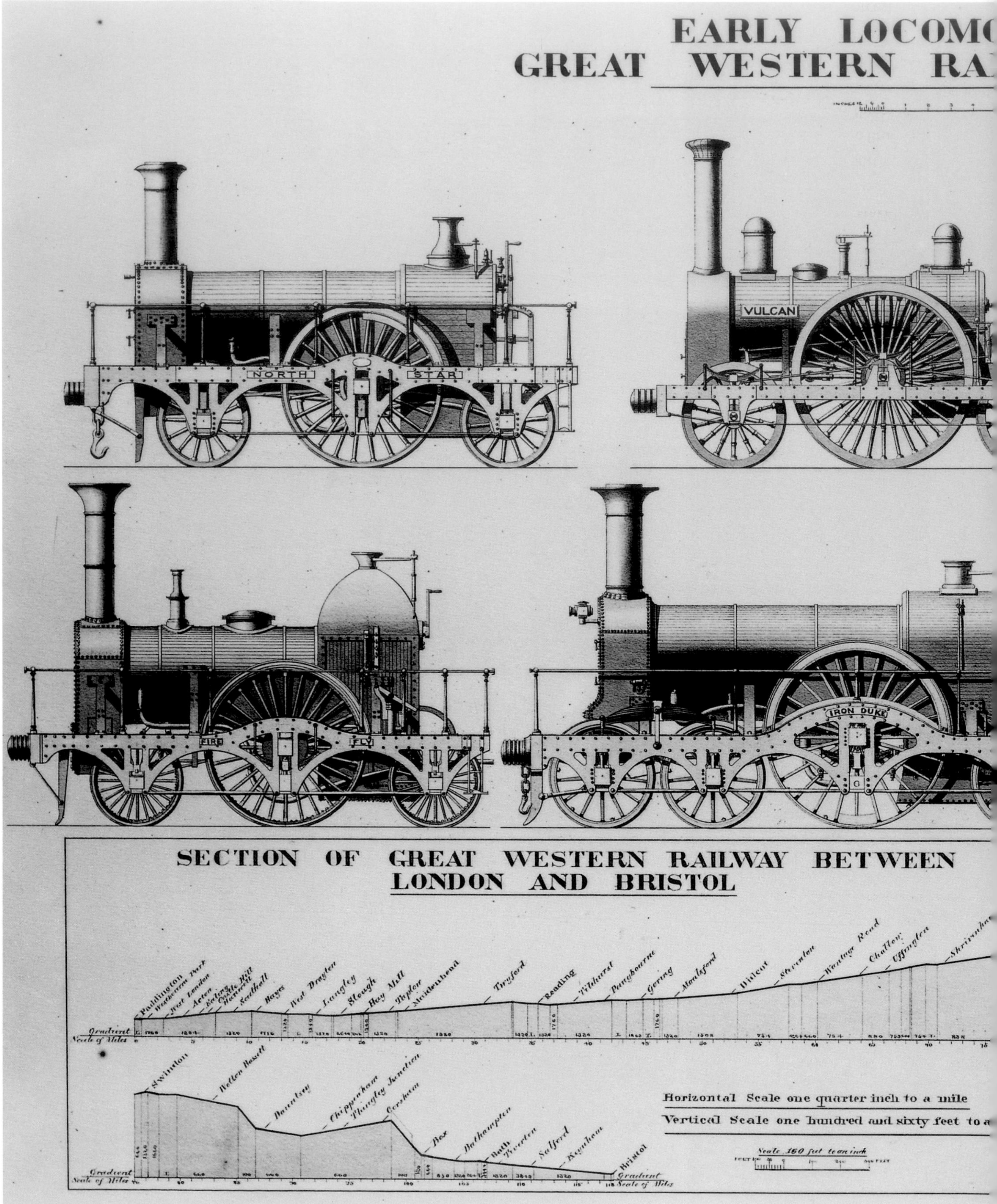
EARLY
GREAT WESTERN
VULCAN
NORTH STAR
FIRE FLY
IRON DUKE
SECTION OF GREAT WESTERN RAILWAY BETWEEN
LONDON AND BRISTOL
Paddington
Westbourne Park
West London
Acton
Ealing
Castle Hill
Hanwell
Southall
Hayes
West Drayton
Langley
Slough
Hay Mill
Taplow
Maidenhead
Twyford
Reading
Tilehurst
Pangbourne
Goring
Moulsford
Didcot
Steventon
Wantage Road
Challow
Uffington
Gradient
Scale of Miles
Swindon
Wotton Bassett
Dauntsey
Chippenham
Thingley Junction
Corsham
Box
Bathampton
Bath
Twerton
Saltford
Keynsham
Bristol
Horizontal Scale one quarter inch to a mile
Vertical Scale one hundred and sixty feet to a
Scale 160 feet to an inch

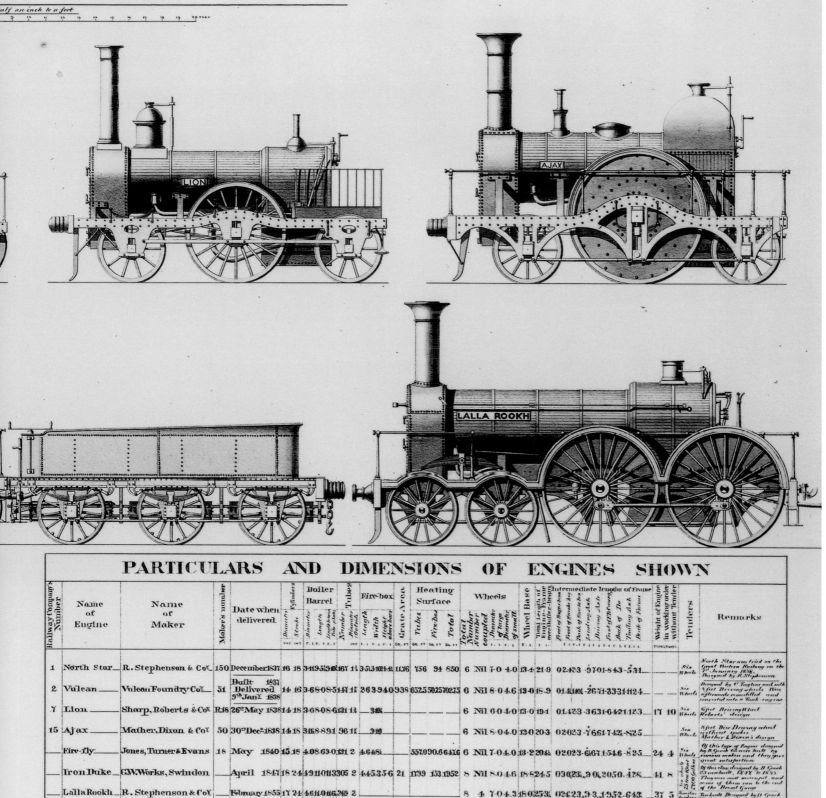

PARTICULARS AND DIMENSIONS OF ENGINES SHOWN

Railway Company Number	Name of Engine	Name of Maker	Maker's number	Date when delivered	Cylinders		Boiler Barrel			Tubes		Fire-box			Grate Area	Heating Surface			Wheels				Wheel Base	Total Length of Engine Frame over buffers beam	Intermediate lengths of frame							Weight of Engine in working order without Tender	Tenders	Remarks
					Diameter	Stroke	Diameter	Length	Length between tube plate	Number	Diameter outside	Length	Width	Height above bars		Tubes	Fire-box	Total	Total Number	Number coupled	Diameter of large	Diameter of small												
1	North Star	R. Stephenson & Co	150	December 1837	16	18	3.11	9.5	9.4	167	1½	3.5	3.10	4.4	11.6	756	94	850	6	Nil	7.0	4.0	13.4	21.9	0.2.4.3.9.7.0.1.8.4.3.5.3.1								Six Wheels	North Star was tried on the Great Western Railway on the 2d January 1838. Designed by R. Stephenson
2	Vulcan	Vulcan Foundry Co	51	Built 1837 Delivered 9th Jan 1838	14	16	3.6	8.0	8.5	141	1½	2.6	3.9	4.0	9.38	652	550	570	6	Nil	8.0	4.6	13.0	18.9	0.1.4.9.0.1.2.6.7.1.3.3.3.1.1.2.4								Six Wheels	Designed by C. Tayleur
7	Lion	Sharp, Roberts & Co	R.18	26th May 1838	14	18	3.6	8.0	8.6	131	1½	3.10							6	Nil	6.0	4.0	13.0	19.4	0.1.4.2.3.3.6.3.6.4.2.1.2.3							17 10	Six Wheels	6 feet Driving Wheel. Roberts' design
15	Ajax	Mather, Dixon & Co	50	30th Dec 1838	14	18	3.11	8.8	9.1	96	1½	3.10							6	Nil	8.0	4.0	13.0	20.3	0.2.0.2.3.7.6.6.1.7.4.2.8.2.5								Six Wheels	8 feet Disc Driving wheel without spokes. Mather & Dixon's design
	Fire-fly	Jones, Turner & Evans	18	May 1840	15	18	4.0	8.6	9.0	131	2	4.6	4.8			557	90.6	641	6	Nil	7.0	4.0	13.2	20.8	0.2.0.2.3.6.6.1.5.4.6.8.2.5							24 4	Six Wheels	Of this type of Engine designed by D. Gooch 62 were built by various makers and they gave great satisfaction
	Iron Duke	G.W. Works, Swindon		April 1847	18	24	4.9	11.0	11.3	305	2	4.4	5.3	5.6	21	1199	153	1952	8	Nil	8.0	4.6	18.8	24.5	0.3.0.2.3.9.0.2.0.5.0.4.2.8							41 8	Six wheels 2 Driven Six wheel Tender	Of this class designed by D. Gooch. These were most successful and some of them ran to the end of the Broad Gauge
	Lalla Rookh	R. Stephenson & Co		February 1855	17	24	4.6	11.0	11.6	249	2								8	4	7.0	4.3	18.0	25.3	0.2.4.2.3.9.3.1.9.5.2.6.4.3							37 5	Similar Tender	Similar. Designed by D. Gooch. 8 feet coupled wheels. Four wheel coupled and six wheels

The report also suggested that, by adopting a wider track gauge, carriages and wagons could be used which had bodies that could be mounted between the rails, rather than projecting over them – thus lowering the centre of gravity of the vehicle and further reducing friction.

An additional advantage to such an approach was that a larger diameter wheel could be employed, again reducing friction. A track gauge of 6ft 10in to 7ft would, Brunel argued, be suitable 'for carriages of all purposes.' The gauge was soon formalised as 7ft ¼ in, although it is not at all clear why the quarter inch was added.

Concluding the report, he did note objections to the adoption of the broad gauge: which he listed as the additional expenses incurred through wider cuttings, embankments and tunnels; a greater amount of friction on curves; additional weight of carriages; and the inconvenience of making a junction with the London & Birmingham Railway (with whom it was hoped the Great Western could share a London terminus). The latter, which Brunel feared would be the biggest obstacle to his scheme, eventually came to nothing, when the London & Birmingham company refused to continue with the scheme and the company were forced to look for a site for their own station in London.

The adoption of what became known as the 'Broad Gauge', was finally ratified by the Board in October 1835, and although common knowledge, was not properly publicised until the following year in a report to the shareholders at the half-yearly meeting held in Bristol in August 1836. To take advantage of the 'very favourable' gradients planned for the line, which were 'unequalled upon any railway of great extent now in progress', the directors, after 'mature consideration', recommended an 'increased width of rails.'

There has been considerable debate regarding Brunel's motives for adopting the broad gauge; it seems likely that in creating his grand design for the Great Western Railway, he felt restricted by the limitations of the old 'coal wagon' gauge, and felt confident in creating something entirely new.

Critics of Brunel have argued that this confidence could be described as arrogance. Adrian Vaughan, in his biography of the engineer, argues that, although the technical excellence of the broad gauge was unquestionable, in this case, Brunel's desire to create a bold and daring alternative to the kind of railway built by Stephenson, overcame his practical engineering sense.

In his evidence to the Gauge Commissioners in 1845, he argued that because of the speeds he contemplated on the new railway, 'the whole machine was too small for the work to be done, and that it required that the parts should be on a scale more commensurate with the mass and velocity to be attained.'

Questioned further, he revealed that 'the impression grew upon me gradually, so it is difficult to fix the time when I first thought a wide gauge desirable.' There is also some evidence that Brunel may also have discussed the matter with his father Marc Isambard, who was pressed into service to assist his son on design work in the early days of the Great Western. The fact that railway tracks on the sawmill operated by Marc Isambard Brunel at Chatham were built to a gauge of 7ft may have been a coincidence, but it seems highly unlikely that father and son had not considered the matter together.

It comes as no surprise that Brunel also had his own ideas about the formation of the broad gauge track work itself. Many early lines like the Liverpool and Manchester Railway had adopted the use of stone blocks fitted with iron chairs to support the rails. Brunel had travelled on

Daniel Gooch's *Arrow* in
Brunel's Bristol Station.
Public Record Office

the Liverpool and Manchester and had not been impressed by the rough ride he experienced, so he proposed his own solution to the problem – the rails were to be supported along the whole of their length using longitudinal timbers.

Cross sleepers known as transoms were fixed at 15ft intervals, and ballast was forced under the timbers to support the track. The whole assembly, which became known as the 'baulk road', was then anchored by wooden piles driven into the ground. The timbers were 'Kyanised', an early form of wood preservation which pre-dated the treating of sleepers with creosote. Brunel also designed the rail itself, an inverted 'U' shape profile known as bridge rail, weighing 43lb per yard.

In 1837 he produced figures which showed that his new track formation cost almost £500 per mile more than the old stone block method, but argued that in using his design, 'the gain in economy, facility and perfection of transport would be cheaply purchased at double the cost.'

The more elaborate nature of the baulk road, coupled with poor weather, meant that the construction of the Great Western line was slower than Brunel and the directors would have liked. It was not until the late spring of 1838 that the first section of line was opened. The first fare-paying train service, from a temporary station at Paddington in West London to Maidenhead, finally ran on Monday 4 June 1838.

Although the railway was launched on a wave of enthusiasm, Brunel and the company soon found themselves in some difficulty, as the performance of both his permanent way and the locomotives used on it proved less than satisfactory. The timber piles used to hold down the track failed and the smooth ride promised by Brunel did not materialise. The rough riding of trains on the railway was compounded by the extremely poor performance of the fleet of locomotives, which were mostly built to Brunel's specification.

When Brunel's extravagant claims as to the advantages of his railway proved false, a group of Great Western shareholders, most based in the North of England and

nicknamed the 'Liverpool Party', used the poor performance of the company in these early days as an excuse to attack both Brunel and his broad gauge. In August 1838, attempts were made by the Liverpool faction to remove the engineer, and the Great Western Board were forced to invite other prominent railway engineers of the day to report on the broad gauge.

Neither Nicholas Wood nor John Hawkshaw (the engineers who reported to the Board) produced enough conclusive evidence to persuade the directors to abandon the broad gauge entirely – although both reports were highly critical of many aspects of the operation of the new railway. Hawkshaw had little good to say about the broad gauge and noted that any company deviating from the standard gauge was in danger of isolating itself – a claim which was to be revived some years later.

Replying to this criticism, Brunel admitted that the gauge question was 'undoubtedly an inconvenience' but that since the GWR was being built in an 'entirely new district in which railways were unknown', and that branch lines were planned to serve areas where railways had not yet reached, this would not be a problem. Once the GWR network was built, he argued, no other lines would be needed, thus avoiding the problem of areas where the two competing gauges would meet.

Wood also argued that the broad gauge was a more expensive proposition, and that the Great Western could convert the existing line at a cost of £123,976 and save a further £156,000 by building the remaining line to standard gauge. Armed with an array of statistics and costs, Brunel was able to easily disprove this argument; noting that the construction of his line would cost little more than a similar standard gauge railway.

Although Brunel had been able to dispute much of Hawkshaw's report, the work done by Nicholas Wood was rather more thorough, including comparative tests on broad and standard gauge locomotives.

The disappointing performance of the broad gauge engines – particularly the Stephenson locomotive 'North Star' (thought to be one of the most powerful and reliable on the railway) – was attributed by Wood to the greater air resistance faced by the larger broad gauge locomotives used by the GWR.

Brunel and his Locomotive Superintendent, Daniel Gooch, were convinced that this was not the case, and eventually discovered that by making modifications to the locomotive blast pipe, its performance could be dramatically improved. In addition, the locomotive's high coke consumption (another weakness identified by Wood), was significantly reduced.

Armed with this evidence, Brunel was able to weather the storm generated by the Liverpool faction, and after a fierce debate the directors recommended 'retaining the width of the gauge with the continuous bearings, as most conducive to the interests of the company.' To improve the ride, they argued that the use of piling should be abandoned and

47

heavier rail of 62lb per mile should be adopted. The shareholders agreed, although by a close margin of 7,790 to 6,145 votes, allowing Brunel's great experiment to continue.

Having survived this close call, Brunel was able to concentrate on the completion of the railway. Work continued, with the line reaching Reading in 1840, and the Great Western Railway finally opened throughout on 30 June 1841. Despite his protestations, Brunel's broad gauge railway was not cheap. The original estimate of the cost of the line was £2,085,330, but in accounts issued by the company on the day the railway opened, the costs were noted as £5,877,120.

Although the choice of the broad gauge could be blamed for some of this overspend (particularly in the design of the trackwork), much of the additional cost was expended on Brunel's choice of route. This reduced gradients where possible and entailed more earthworks, tunnels and bridges, than a route which followed the contours of the landscape more closely. The end result was, as A.H. Malan wrote, a railway 'eminently suited for high speed', with curves of a large radius, and no gradient steeper than 1 in 660, except two inclines of 1 in 100 at Box and Wootton Bassett, where extra engine power was to be employed.

Even before the Great Western Railway was complete, Brunel had begun the task of engineering other railways to his broad gauge designs. The Bristol & Exeter opened in 1844, and was followed by the Cheltenham & Great Western Union

Railway, the South Devon Railway, the Cornwall and West Cornwall Railways and the South Wales Railway; thus creating a broad gauge empire stretching across the West Country. The planning and creation of this empire led to what became known as the 'Battle of the Gauges', a controversy which was to dominate the railway world for almost a decade.

This dispute was aggravated by 'breaks of gauge' – places where the broad gauge and standard gauge met. In 1845, ten were recorded, and at locations such as Gloucester, passengers were forced to leave their standard gauge train to cross the platform to a broad gauge service for the rest of their journey.

Quite apart from the gauge question, the dispute was fuelled by the fact that rival companies, such as the London & North Western Railway and the London & South Western Railway, were unwilling to allow the Great Western to make deep inroads into what they considered to be their territory. It was at Gloucester that the first skirmishes of the 'Battle of the Gauges' took place.

The first signs of trouble had been seen in the activities of the Bristol and Gloucester Railway, a line initially intended to be standard gauge. Under pressure from Brunel, who was also their engineer, the company decided in 1843 to adopt the broad gauge.

Brunel argued that the break of gauge at Gloucester (between the broad gauge of the Great Western Railway and the standard gauge of the Birmingham & Gloucester Railway) could be easily overcome by a simple arrangement to

transfer goods from one wagon to another. Passengers would, he argued, 'merely step from one carriage into the other and on the same platform.'

As usual, Brunel's rather offhand remark was not completely satisfactory, and the arrangement he mentioned for goods handling, although sketched in his notebooks, never appeared. Delays and disruption occurred in the small goods depot and the problems experienced were subsequently exaggerated and exploited by Brunel's opponents. Further difficulties occurred when the Bristol & Gloucester Railway joined forces with the Birmingham and Gloucester Railway in January 1845. The new Bristol & Birmingham Railway then set about negotiations with the Great Western Railway, in order to extend the broad gauge to Birmingham. No satisfactory deal could be agreed and the line was subsequently purchased by the Midland Railway; thus ending Brunel's aim of broad gauge travel from Bristol to Birmingham and confirming Gloucester as a break of gauge.

Two more battles raised the stakes over the gauge question. In 1844, two further new schemes were proposed north of Oxford. Both were important to Brunel and his opponents, since they threatened to carry the broad gauge deep into the heart of what its supporters disparagingly called 'narrow gauge' territory.

The first was the Oxford, Worcester & Wolverhampton Railway, whose committee of management included three Great Western directors. Although the promoters of this line hoped to generate much income from passenger traffic, it was the prospect of linking the rich industrial West Midlands with the capital, which was more attractive.

The prospectus, issued in September 1844, noted that the new line would serve not just collieries, ironworks and other industrial concerns, but also a large agricultural region. The map included in the prospectus also showed the route of the second and equally contentious railway; a line linking Oxford & Rugby by way of Banbury – the Oxford and Rugby Railway.

In June 1845, Richard Cobden MP, a fierce opponent of the broad gauge, persuaded parliament that the whole question of a uniform gauge for railways should be investigated by a Royal Commission. Three commissioners were appointed: Sir Frederick Smith, the first Inspector-General of Railways to the Board of Trade, Peter Barlow, Professor of Mathematics at The Military Academy at Woolwich; and George Airey, the Astronomer Royal. The commission was asked to recommend whether future railway acts should contain a reference to a uniform track gauge, the practicability of creating one uniform gauge for the country as a whole, and any solutions they might have for the 'Break of Gauge' problem.

Most of the conclusions reached by the Commission were arrived at after interviewing expert witnesses – a veritable railway 'Who's Who' of the period. Hardened opponents of the broad gauge, such as Robert Stephenson, lost no opportunity to criticise it. He argued that

'its introduction has involved the country in very great inconvenience', with the break of gauge being its greatest disadvantage, as well as the increased cost of construction of broad gauge lines and rolling stock.

Brunel was called to give evidence on 25 October 1845, answering a total of 200 questions. Having been questioned as to why he had chosen the broad gauge in the first place, he was then asked if he had to build the Great Western Railway again, would he still choose the 7ft gauge? Brunel replied that he was likely to be accused of recklessness, since 'I should rather be above than under seven feet now, if I had to reconstruct the lines'. To the argument that broad gauge railways were proportionately larger, and therefore more expensive to build, Brunel claimed that differences between broad and narrow were negligible.

On the question of a uniform gauge for the whole country, he was less clear – contradicting himself in the course of one answer, by arguing that there would be some advantage to a 'similarity of gauge', since it would rid railways of the problem of changing from one system to the other, but that a great deal of progress had been made on railways through competition between promoters of the rival gauges. Many historians have argued, however, that it was the quality of Gooch's locomotives and the well-engineered line designed by Brunel, which brought about improvement on the Great Western, not the track gauge – so his assertion that competition brought about improvement was not entirely satisfactory.

Robert Stephenson, Brunel's friend and professional rival, in the 1850s. Stephenson built all his railways using the 4' 8½" gauge. *National Railway Museum*

49

In relation to the problem of the break of gauge, it was clear that Brunel did not see the Great Western and its associated railways as part of a national railway network, but rather as a regional system within which passengers and goods could travel, changing at particular locations to other lines.

Brunel argued that:

If a network of railways … over England is made, I think it will be impossible that passenger carriages can be running in all directions over that network without changing … The spirit of emulation and competition … will do more good than that uniformity of system which has been so much talked of the last two or three years.

Although, as already noted, passengers were much inconvenienced by having to change trains at places like Gloucester, the 'Break of Gauge Question' had a far greater impact on goods traffic. The average delay for goods at Gloucester was estimated at between four and five hours, during which time they were manhandled from one train to another, with material either lost or damaged in the process. Brunel admitted that 'some inconvenience may occur' but argued that he had a solution for the problem, which involved the use of what we might today call container traffic; whereby wagon bodies could be lifted from one wagon chassis to another at transhipment depots. If this method was not suitable, Brunel suggested the use of a broad gauge transporter truck, with narrow gauge rails set into it, to carry, as he put it, 'wagon and all'.

Asked if this idea would cause problems, he dismissed the questioner, claiming that there would be little practical difficulty. A wagon with telescopic axles to run on both gauges was also proposed. Gooch in his diaries wrote, 'I never had any faith in any of these plans as workable in practice.'

Before completing his session as a witness, Brunel had to defend himself against some awkward questions regarding other projects in which he was involved, where he had not recommended the use of the broad gauge.

As well as the railway from Genoa to Turin, he had also become the engineer of the Taff Vale Railway in South Wales, in 1836, which had been built as standard gauge from its inception. To critics who pointed out this inconsistency, Brunel merely argued that the main advantage of the broad gauge was the fact that its trains could run at consistently faster speeds, and had rolling stock which was of greater capacity and more comfortable. On both the lines mentioned high speeds were not a high priority: so, he concluded, they did not necessarily have to be broad gauge.

Before the end of proceedings, Brunel managed to persuade the commissioners to arrange a series of trials to test the worth of locomotives of both gauges. A Gooch *Firefly* class *Ixion* was matched against a Stephenson *Long Boiler* locomotive Number 54. The broad gauge engine outperformed its Stephenson rival easily in terms of both average and top speeds, with the unfortunate Number 54 even derailing itself on one trip. The data obtained on these trials was added to a wealth of other statistical information supplied by both sides – costs of

Broad gauge locomotives at Swindon in 1898, awaiting scrapping or conversion. Several miles of sidings had to be laid to accommodate the redundant engines and stock.
National Railway Museum

THE BATTLE OF THE GAUGES

construction, running costs, locomotive and train performance and traffic statistics were all submitted – and the commissioners had the unenviable task of absorbing and considering all the conflicting material, as well as the testimony of the various witnesses called.

In 1846, the commissioners finally reported. They prefaced their findings by noting that they could find little to fault with the broad gauge itself – there was little doubt that with regard to safety, speed and 'the convenience of passengers' it was superior to the narrow gauge and that 'the public are mainly indebted for the present rate of speed and the increased accommodation of the railway carriages to the genius of Mr Brunel and the liberality of the Great Western Railway'.

Then came the bad news. Whilst the impressive performance of broad gauge express trains was inescapable, they were for the accommodation of 'a comparatively small number of persons'. This was of less importance than the 'general commercial traffic of the country' and therefore, in the matter of the transportation of goods, the commissioners believed that the narrow gauge was better suited for the movement of goods.

Amongst the welter of statistical information that had been submitted to the commission, one of the most important was the fact that up to July 1845, only 274 miles of broad gauge line had been built (compared to 1,901 miles of standard gauge), and the question of a uniform gauge was already a pressing reality. Thus, the commissioners ruled:

If it were imperative to produce uniformity, we should recommend that uniformity be produced by an alteration of the broad to narrow gauge.

The decision caused dismay amongst supporters of the broad gauge who had hoped that they would win the day. Incensed, Brunel, aided by Gooch, swiftly wrote a 43-page pamphlet 'Observations on the Report of the Gauge Commissioners'. In it, Brunel refuted many of the reports findings and accused the commissioners of ignoring the

evidence which supporters of the broad gauge had submitted.

'Facts are stubborn things' he wrote, and he carefully exposed every mistake and assumption made. Brunel further argued that it would be wrong for the gauge of lines already sanctioned by parliament, to now be changed, and there should be 'a strong protest against any legislative interference with the broad-gauge system.'

There is some evidence that the efforts of Brunel and the Great Western may have caused parliament to water down some of the conclusions of the Royal Commission, with the passing of 'An Act for the Regulating the Gauge of Railways' in July 1846. Although 4ft 8½in was specified as the gauge of all new railways in Great Britain, the new Bill further specified that this gauge would be the standard unless any present or future Act had a 'special enactment defining the gauge' contained within it.

This clause left the door open for future broad gauge lines to be built, a process which was to continue for some years. The two lines which had precipitated the debate in the first place, the Oxford, Worcester & Wolverhampton and the Oxford & Rugby, were allowed to proceed as planned.

The arrangement seemed to be a partial reprieve for the broad gauge, but defined the limits of Brunel's broad gauge empire – any thought of it penetrating as far north as the River Mersey was now gone. Furthermore, as the national railway network grew ever larger, the Great Western found it harder and harder

to maintain the haughty isolation it had once enjoyed. Increasingly 'mixed' gauge track with three rails allowing the passage of both gauges was introduced, and with the acquisition of standard gauge lines by the Great Western in the 1850s, the long term future of the broad gauge was in doubt.

Few would doubt the skill and flair displayed by Brunel in the design of his broad gauge railway. His decision not to use the standard gauge was something of a gamble, and in the end, for all its theoretical advantages, the broad gauge was introduced too late to really make an impact nationally and for the gamble to pay off.

The creation of the broad gauge also left the company with a considerable financial burden. From the 1860s onwards, a programme of conversion began – a process which cost the Great Western Railway large sums of money. Track work, locomotives, carriages and wagons all had to be either rebuilt (or in many cases scrapped) and replacements built. This conversion process ultimately inhibited development of the railway until the early years of the twentieth century.

The creation of the broad gauge also created a national problem for both railway companies and government. The existance of two separate gauges on one national railway network could not be tolerated; and, for all the advantages of speed, comfort and safety enjoyed by Brunel's broad gauge, the far larger mileage of the standard gauge meant that there could only be one standard gauge

for the country – the one introduced by Stephenson in 1825.

Brunel died in 1859. Having fought for his broad gauge in 1838 and 1846 it was perhaps fortunate that he did not live to see its decline and eventual extinction. Some 33 years after the death of its creator, on the weekend of 20 and 21 May 1892, the process was completed when the whole of Brunel's main line from Paddington to Penzance was converted to the standard gauge – thus ending his great experiment for good.

Even in 1942, fifty years after the end of the broad gauge, one author argued that the Great Western Railway from its beginning 'commanded universal esteem because it was a giant among things, planned and executed by giants who were giants even in their mistakes.' Brunel, the writer continued, 'could only err magnificently, as he did, if he did, in his 7ft gauge.'

Critics today, just as they were over 150 years ago, are still divided on the merits of the broad gauge – an issue that was to dominate the history of the railway planned and built by perhaps the most flamboyant and talented engineer of his generation.

A GAUGE TOO FAR OR A GAUGE TOO LATE/EARLY?

Vic Stephens

When the Great Western Railway (GWR) agreed to build a 7ft gauge, did Brunel deliberately set out to be different from the establishment, as was his wont on occasions, or was it flair and enterprising engineering brilliance that convinced him to proceed with 7ft gauge? Brunel was once quoted as saying, '7ft gauge is the best and Stephenson has got it wrong'.

In his report to the GWR Board in August 1838 Brunel wrote:

It has been asserted that 4ft 8in, the width adopted on the Liverpool and Manchester Railway, is exactly the proper width for all railways, and that to adopt any other dimension is to deviate from a positive rule which experience has proved correct; but such an assertion can be maintained by no reasoning. Admitting, for the sake of argument, that, under the particular circumstances in which it has been tried, 4 feet 8 inches has been proved the best possible dimension, the question would still remain – What are the best dimensions under the circumstances?

How true this is one will never know, but there are some hard facts that suggest that, maybe, just maybe, there was some truth in what Brunel said. Historians and railway experts have argued for years the rights and wrongs of both cases.

Was the decision in favour of the standard gauge of 4ft 8½in based on good engineering data or commercial realism? If not on engineering grounds what were the reasons and why were they considered more acceptable?

Did broad gauge have the potential to provide a better railway, and was it defeated on engineering grounds or by commercial pressures?

The passage of time has coloured history writers' views as to the correcct

version of events; but engineering facts speak louder than any account of events in Brunel's times. The argument as to the respective merits of the two gauges has been picked over many times over the years, but essentially boils down to the following:

FACT 1

Brunel had decided that Stephenson's locomotives were too slow at only 35mph. He was seeking to achieve 60mph and perhaps more. Brunel believed that engines and carriages designed with a low centre of gravity and wide-apart wheels would prove to be extremely stable at high speeds. He placed great emphasis on this to the GWR Board and on his ability to provide carriages and locomotives that were both comfortable and fast.

Travelling times can be compared to prove Brunel's argument:

London to Birmingham:
112 miles standard gauge
Travel time 1838   5½ hours
Travel time 1850   3 hours

London to Bristol:
118 mile broad gauge
Travel time 1841   4 hours 10minutes
Travel time 1850   2 hours 35 minutes

The need for high speed vehicles to have a low centre of gravity and wheels as large as possible, remains a constant headache for designers of railway vehicles, even in the twenty-first century.

BROAD GAUGE 15 – STANDARD GAUGE 0

FACT 2

An additional unwritten benefit of the wider carriages was that more passengers could be accommodated in each carriage, thus requiring fewer vehicles, less maintenance and less cost to the railway.

BROAD GAUGE 30 – STANDARD GAUGE 0

FACT 3

Brunel and his locomotive designer Daniel Gooch had calculated that the larger wheels that were possible with broad gauge, meant that less traction force was required to move the vehicles: 18lb compared with 40lb for standard gauge. A reduction in friction of this magnitude also meant that vehicles imparted less damage to the track.

The quality of the GWR track was a constant embarrassment to Brunel. It was often said that broad gauge trains caused the damage, but, in reality, it was more likely to be the design of the track sub-structure which used an inferior construction method.

Modifications to the sub-structure solved most of these problems, suggesting that broad gauge itself should not be blamed but rather the initial design of the track bed.

BROAD GAUGE 40 – STANDARD GAUGE 0

FACT 4

The land requirements for the construction of a 7ft broad-gauge railway were acknowledged to be greater than for a standard gauge of 4ft 8½in. broad gauge an additional 6% land take and a consequential increase in engineering costs. The GWR infrastructure is recognised as being 30 % larger than Stephenson's Liverpool & Manchester Railway infrastructure.

For Stephenson, an average tunnel was 24ft across, while for Brunel it was 30ft. However, Brunel's tunnels were of such immense proportions that the gauge probably made little or no difference to the cost of their construction.

The larger infrastructure doubtless did cost more, with price differentials from 10% to 100% often quoted. The truth of this is impossible to establish.

It is clear, however, that Brunel continued to construct grand structures which where far in excess of minimum requirements, and kept finding himself in conflict with both his supporters and the accountants.

BROAD GAUGE 40 – STANDARD GAUGE 15

FACT 5

During the great gauge debate, standard gauge lines were in ascendancy and flourishing, while the broad gauge break-points saw much activity with the transfer between the gauges.

For passengers this was not a major issue but where freight was concerned it was proving a hindrance to the generation of new traffic, a source of irritation to existing traffic and a major expense for any freight client with a departure point or destination on the broad gauge.

BROAD GAUGE 40 – STANDARD GAUGE 30

FACT 6

To settle the debate, the government of the day set up a commission to review all the arguments being put forward by both camps. Substantial evidence was collected for the commission but two key factors in the debate were:

1) the large number of lawyers representing the standard gauge lobby
2) the lack of engineering understanding of the commissioners

The Gauge Commissioners reported to parliament in 1846 that, whilst they found that broad gauge engineering did represent a better solution, the spread of the standard gauge was now so overwhelming that it would be in the majority interest to adopt it as the only gauge for the country's railways.

DEUCE

FACT 7

Brunel refused to give in easily to these recommendations. Together with others (Gooch and Saunders being the most important) he issued 50 pages of 'Observations on the Report'. Neither, indeed, did parliament fully agree with the commissioners' report.

ADVANTAGE – BROAD GAUGE

FACT 8

A Board of Trade review finally recommended that only lines connected to the GWR should be broad gauge. Remaining lines throughout the country should be standard gauge.

An important exception to this was the Oxford to Wolverhampton Railway, which was required to be laid to dual gauge but built to standard.

DEUCE

FACT 9

Parliament accepted the findings of the Board of Trade review and passed the Gauge Act, allowing GWR broad gauge but requiring gauge elsewhere to be standard.

ADVANTAGE – STANDARD GAUGE

FACT 10

When Brunel died in 1859 the GWR lost its chief advocate of broad gauge. Ten years later the GWR had finally to concede to standard gauge. The commercial pressure applied by its clients made it impossible to support and follow its engineers' adherence to the better engineering solution.

The directors of the GWR, having fully depreciated their broad gauge assets, converted their railway fully to standard gauge in October 1892.

GAME, SET AND MATCH

Umpire's Report:

The benefits for today's railway of Brunel's engineering enterprise is that infrastructure changes to accommodate new, larger vehicles, require substantially less alteration on former GWR Broad gauge routes than they do in the rest of the country. Indeed, unlike the majority of UK railway tunnels, Brunel's tunnels are usually sufficiently large not to require alteration for today's high-speed and wide-bodied freight trains and cause few aerodynamic problems.

Was the decision therefore correct for the engineering of 1846, but lacking in forward vision – or was it financially driven by the greater expenditure required to convert standard to broad gauge? We will never know but can surmise the following:

1 If broad gauge had been used earlier, say by horses and carts, history might have been different. The first evidence of a 4ft 8½in 'gauge' can be found in Assyrian artefacts, where evidence of stone cart-ways exists.

2 Standard gauge was used predominately in the industrial areas of the UK, where there was greater financial power and probably commercial pressure to remain standard.

3 The fact that the Board of Trade allowed the GWR to continue with broad gauge indicates that there must have been doubts in the minds of its officials that the standard gauge solution was the most appropriate.

Finally, it is interesting to note that the debate regarding the merits of the railway in Brunel's era, is the same debate that has occurred in our own time concerning the high-speed railways of the world, as in Japan, on the Shinkansen Lines.

4 PADDINGTON
'A STATION AFTER MY OWN FANCY'

Peter Quartermaine

WHEN THE GREAT WESTERN Railway's line from London to Bristol finally opened in June 1838, its powerful locomotives, designed by Daniel Gooch (who, like Brunel, was then only in his twenties), were easily the fastest in the world, capable of an everyday speed of well over sixty miles per hour. The line was extended to Exeter in 1844, and even from there, London could be reached in just five hours (today it takes two and a half).

For most people in Britain today, especially since Lord Beeching famously axed so many rural lines in the 1960s, the railways are associated almost inevitably with decline and re-use.

The very term 'railway' is as likely to be associated with heritage as with transport. It was not always so. Certainly the scope, style and function of Paddington Station as originally built, cannot fully be understood without reference to the 'railway mania' that periodically swept the country's stock exchange during the last century.

London's great nineteenth-century railway termini were 'cathedrals of industrial architecture', as John Betjeman called them back in 1972. Railway stations displayed a pride in technical innovation which is nowhere better exemplified, than in Brunel's finest work for the Great Western Railway – Paddington Station.

Like the architects of the Georgian Age, he was a master designer; he assumed responsibility for the form and character of everything connected with the railway – stations, signals, bridges and tunnels: he gave coherence to the railway landscape, and like all great designers had an impeccable sense of style.[1]

Opened on 16 January 1854, Paddington Station was completed between the peak of one investment wave in 1847, and another, in 1865–66. In the five years from 1840 'railway expenditure consumed about half of total domestic capital formation', and between 1837 and 1842, 'investment in railways exceeded the value of Britain's total exports to the United States.'[2]

One aspect of that period, all too familiar in our own culture, is that of private rail companies in fierce competition, and Brunel's station – built as it was under constant time and financial pressures from Great Western's Board of Directors – was planned to outdo the Great Northern Railway's new terminus at Euston, which had opened in 1846.

As Betjeman noted, all the railway companies, 'even if their origins were in provincial towns, were determined to make a big splash when they reached the capital'. So Paddington was designed to be the impressive metropolitan terminus of a company whose name Brunel envisaged from the start as encompassing steamship services from Bristol to New York. 'Western' was for him oceanic in its scope: his paddle steamer *Great Western* was to reach New York in fifteen days in 1838, and the pioneering *Great Britain* and *Great Eastern* would follow.

Philip Hardwick's great Doric arch at Euston, had served architecturally as a formal entrance from the traditional city to the technologically advanced environment of the railway – a city gate onto a brave new world. Paddington would boast no such freestanding symbol

of progress, but in its very materials and facilities for passengers (in which Euston was sadly lacking) would claim to be the pre-eminent London terminus.

A temporary wooden building (also by Brunel) had been in use at Paddington since 1837. But the forward-looking scale and practicality of his new Paddington station have allowed it to be reborn in this millennium – extensively restored and with a new direct rail-link and airline check-in to Heathrow airport – developments which he would have relished.

Also transformed, is the passenger concourse at 'The Lawn'; a name deriving from the stationmaster's original garden there in the 1840s. Its new multi-level facilities make imaginative use of the station's grand spans – inviting passengers to linger high within them and enjoy the ebb and flow of trains and people alike, as vital elements of the city's life.

Brunel's original design restricted such an overview to the elegant Moorish bay window of the Directors' Room on Platform 1, but the new development owes much to those great urban covered spaces of our own times, the galleria and the shopping mall.

Interestingly, these also both derive ultimately from Joseph Paxton's Great Exhibition building of 1851, whose fan-shaped glass end wall is today an architectural cliché.

A railway terminus, whatever its other facilities, has its life and being in movement; trains come and go, and people move through it with varied purpose and urgency. As a city structure, then, every aspect of Paddington's design and function has to do with locomotion.

The sheer planning and technology required to enable a train to slide smoothly away for faraway destinations has always been truly daunting.

The very route of the Great Western Railway demanded extraordinary surveying and engineering, in often-difficult terrain, with Brunel working with his assistants throughout the summer of 1833, charting the route to Bristol. The challenge was immense, and difficult for us now to grasp – history 'holds no previous record of engineering adventure on such a scale.'[3] The conquest of planetary, rather than inter-city, space in our own times offers some parallels, but has left no usable monuments, no such accessible and varied legacy of structures, which we can regard with affection as part of our everyday environment. At the time, though, the railway not only changed the world, but the very way people might see it.

The Royal Albert Bridge over the River Tamar at Saltash, begun in 1853 and opened in 1859 [see Chapter 6], remains the most dramatic example of Brunel's engineering skill on the Great Western line. But also along its route are tunnels, viaducts and embankments, and even sea defences, which constantly adjust a varied landscape to the gentle gradients required by a steam railway.

The thin steel rails are threaded through or over obstacles with a skill that makes our progress by train seem effortless, inevitable. Such seemingly magical transit radically changed how the first passengers perceived landscape, just as car, and later, air travel, would change it yet again. 'The railroad did not appear embedded in the space of the landscape the way coach and highway are, but seemed to strike its way through it.'[4]

So, for example, the great stone-faced embankment that carries the Great Western line beneath the soft red cliffs from Teignmouth to Exmouth has thrilled countless holidaymakers and others since, in 1846, it first offered passengers its dramatic ocean views from just behind the beach itself. It not only provides unique views of landscape and seascape, but is also a dramatically engineered interface between the two. Yet if 'the railroad opened up new spaces that were not easily accessible before', it did so by 'destroying space, namely the space between points'. To board a train at Paddington over 150 years ago was to enter a new technological capsule en-route for destinations west.[5]

In 1880, the expansion of the railways brought about the standardisation of time itself. Previously, the clocks on town halls throughout the country's regions had shown slightly varying hours. The revolutionary speed of the new train travel, however, meant that everyone had to keep the same time if the train timetables were to make any sense.

And, aside from such new principles of standardisation, the integrated civil engineering of the railway system – its tunnels, bridges, signals, viaducts, country stations, city termini – revolutionised the very appearance of the world.

Contemporary society viewed these constructions as radical, but today they are regarded, often somewhat romantically, as monuments of 'a brief heroic age of engineering as remote from our world as that of the great medieval cathedrals.'[6]

The best of this engineering, such as Paddington itself, while often monumental in scale and purpose,

The first Paddington Station, 1838–54.
Public Record Office

The Railway Station
by William Frith, 1863,
showing a broad gauge
train and gas lighting
at Paddington.
Leicester City
Museums Service

'A STATION AFTER MY OWN FANCY'

remains a vital and everyday part of the working legacy that nineteenth-century planning and craftsmanship have bequeathed to today's transport network. In sheer practical terms, it is today hard to imagine where Britain would be without it.

Above all, the railway developments of the nineteenth century facilitated the efficient movement of people (though initially only the well-to-do) and the age's new 'edifices of glass architecture – railroad stations, market halls, exhibition palaces, arcades – served as places of transit and storage.'[7] Paddington's train sheds, 'Brunel's great greenhouse', as Betjeman affectionately called them, survive as his most important buildings.

This was an age in which the technology of which we are now so wary seemed to offer unlimited possibilities, though the changes brought about in both the visible environment and in the spheres of science and religion, caused unease as well as excitement.

By 1851, Britain was the first nation in which more people lived in the towns than in the country. This urban concentration meant that construction of any railway station in a major city involved extensive land purchase and demolition, as much for the incoming railway lines as for the station complex itself. The writer Charles Dickens had recorded the traumatic impact of building works for the new line into Euston – and also the feverish fascination that accompanied them – in his novel *Dombey and Son*, published between 1846 and 1848:

The newly opened station at Paddington, 1854.
Illustrated London New s

The first shock of a great earthquake had, just at that period, rent the whole neighbourhood to its centre. Traces of its course were visible on every side. Houses were knocked down; streets broken through and stopped; deep pits and trenches dug in the ground; enormous heaps of earth and clay thrown up; buildings that were undermined and shaking, propped up by great beams of wood.

It has been estimated that in Britain's five major cities, 'the railways had consumed between 5.2 and 9.0 per cent of the 1840 built-up area by 1900 and acquired much larger acreage in the peripheral areas beyond', while in the eight years from 1842 to 1850 'the number of passengers carried trebled, and freight tonnage increased sevenfold.'[8]

Moreover, compared with horse-drawn services, rail travel offered a dramatically different approach to the very heart of those cities it both served and stimulated. The countrywide network of coaching inns were fully integrated into the local life and architecture of their setting, in both scale and function. By contrast, train travel both needed and created a new world – and of this world, Paddington remains one of the greatest architectural expressions.

In the 1850s Paddington was at the very edge of the city. Today the station is hard to see, tightly woven as it is into the fabric and traffic of the inner city. Betjeman observed that Paddington was 'the only London terminus with no exterior.' Indeed, for those arriving by train, Brunel's station is in one sense little more than neutral space to be traversed on the way to a destination – probably by the Underground system he had himself foreseen.[9]

Apart from lacking a grand facade (unlike its rival, the magnificent

St Pancras, built in 1868), the new Paddington station also had the disadvantage of being built in a cutting, so that passengers still descend to it from street level. The starkly functional engineering which links the station proper to westward destinations as far as Penzance (though no longer, alas, New York) is deliberately masked by the facade for the Great Western Hotel, designed by Philip Charles Hardwick, who had also worked with his father on the Euston arch. The hotel is itself notable as the first purpose-built hotel in Britain, and was seen at its opening in June 1854 as 'the largest and most sumptuous' in England.[10]

But the very city environment that now presses against it on all sides makes Paddington, of all Brunel's works, the one most in need of reappraisal – especially since its upgrading and restoration have emphasised that elegant, uninterrupted, longitudinal space – so crucial to its function as an efficient rail terminus.

The original drawings for Paddington were, for years, stored at the station itself in smoky rooms above the tracks. Many are now in poor condition and some lost. But the surviving drawings possess the rich and reassuring materiality of meticulously draughted nuts, bolts and girders and of stone and brick and wood.

For instance, every detail of the frame, sill and bars of a window opening – even the full-size design for a small, functional, metal ventilator – is finely drawn and precisely specified.

Driving such attention to detail is a vision which deploys materials and technology to meet the overall service needs of the Great Western Railway – whilst never forgetting that most practical of needs – an impressive terminus building in the capital.

The roof spans designed for Paddington by Brunel represented a state-of-the-art use of materials that were themselves the very mark of the new age: iron and glass. Both railway trains, and the new structures needed to accommodate them, were eloquent expressions of innovative technological developments brought about by the industrial revolution.

Just as travel by train challenged traditional perceptions of time and space, so those functional iron and glass structures that served the hot and smoking locomotives had a translucence and purity that excited – and just as often shocked – those more accustomed to an architecture of traditional solidity and ornament.

Some, like Ruskin, held that such constructions were not architecture at all, but mere engineering; however, it is a measure of Brunel's talent that his work combined both function and beauty. The elegance of the constructions themselves is matched by that of the engineering drawings produced by the draughtsmen for the engineers to work from. Some drawings, several of the Royal Albert Bridge, for example, carry calculations and sketches in their margins – on the spot struggles to fit the plan to the reality of the site.

At Paddington, Brunel collaborated with the architect Matthew Digby Wyatt, who was to be responsible for the

The Great Western Royal Hotel at Paddington, c.1905. It was designed by Philip Hardwick and completed in 1852.
National Railway Museum

Tracery at the
'Town end', Paddington.
P. Quartermaine

architectural detailing. In a much-quoted letter of 13 January 1851, Brunel writes:

> I am going to design, in a great hurry, and I believe to build, a Station after my own fancy; that is, with engineering roofs, etc. It is at Paddington, in a cutting, and admitting of no exterior, all interior and all roofed in. Now, such a thing will be entirely <u>metal</u> as to all the general forms, arrangements and design; it almost of necessity becomes an Engineering Work, but, to be honest, even if it were not, it is a branch of architecture of which I am fond, and, of course, believe myself fully competent for; but for <u>detail</u> of ornamentation I neither have the time nor knowledge, and with all my confidence in my own ability I have never any objection to advice and assistance even in the department which I keep t myself, namely the general design.

In another letter of 30 December, that same year, Brunel was already defending his position to the Great Western Board, stressing that in a railway 'the only works to be constructed are engineering works, and there can really only be one engineer.' It was an aesthetic, as well as practical, position that was to have its finest expression there 'at Paddington, in a cutting.'

In July 1850, Brunel had been a member of the committee which finally chose the similarly revolutionary design, submitted by Joseph Paxton, to house the 1851 Great Exhibition of Art and Industry in London. This 'Crystal Palace', as Punch first termed it in November 1850, stood in Hyde Park from 1851 until moved to Sydenham the following year. Significantly, the creator of the now-legendary Crystal Palace was, like Brunel, no architect. Paxton's expertise lay in the design of highly original greenhouses, built on a grand scale, for the age's great collectors of rare trees and plants, notably the Duke of Devonshire.

However, it was Paxton's famously simple design for a prefabricated sectional building of iron and glass for the Great Exhibition that was to change the nature of architecture itself; and Brunel (who had himself submitted an unsuccessful design for the Great Exhibition building) chose the contractors for Paxton's design, Fox, Henderson and Company, to construct Paddington.

Grand in scale and function Paddington may be, but, as always with Brunel, every last detail was carefully planned. For example; one dimension of the station now, sadly, completely lost, was Brunel's integration of the Paddington Canal basin into what we would now term the 'transport infrastructure' of the site. …

Running alongside the northern edge of the station, this canal was used both for transporting goods and for bringing in the vast quantities of coal needed each day.

The great covered urban expanses of metropolitan railway stations offered a new stage for the enactment of a consciously modern city life, and one that was recorded by painters of the period in many countries. The rich and famous were often to be seen there, for the railway station was one definer of a new and modern urbanity.

Queen Victoria, herself a great promoter of train travel, had made her very first train journey to the previous Paddington building as early as June 1842. Fifty-nine years later, a black-draped train

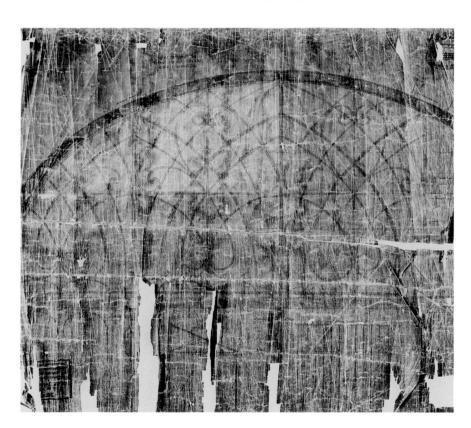

Above:
The development of the Lawn at Paddington.
Nick Hufton / VIEW

Plan of tracery at the ends of the station.
Railtrack

'A STATION AFTER MY OWN FANCY'

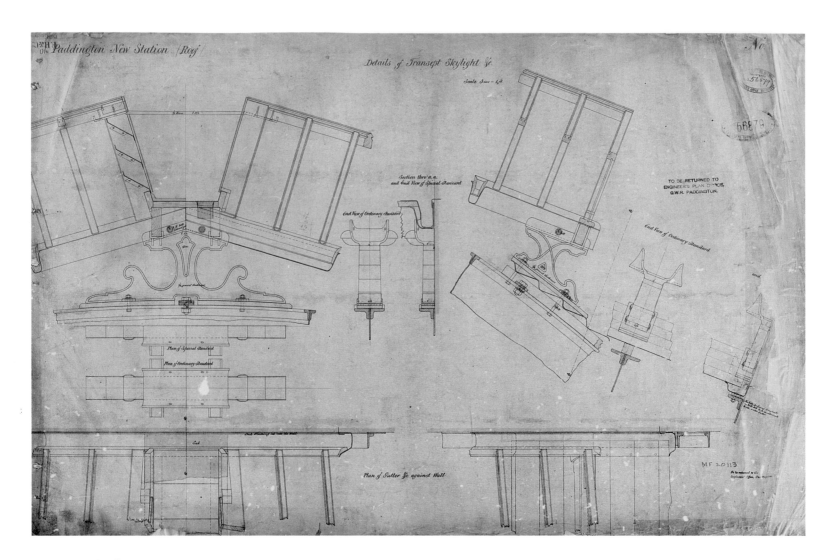

Fox, Henderson plan of
skylight details. *Railtrack*

Paddington roof today
P. Quartermaine

Transverse section of
Paddington. *Railtrack*

would bring her coffin there from Windsor Castle.

But it was not only the famous who passed through such a station. The artist, William Powell Frith, in his monumental painting, *The Railway Station*, set at Paddington, celebrated this social phenomenon.

By the time this painting was displayed to the public in 1862, nearly 10,000 miles of track were open, with some 170 million railway-passengers using it that year. Frith himself had commented frostily, 'I don't think the station at Paddington can be called picturesque'.

For those viewers in 1858, though, a railway station was an exciting and accessible microcosm of the technology shaping their now irreversibly industrial lives – familiar, certainly, but strangely tinged with the heroic. In this life the humble train commuter would henceforth play an essential role – one which was only made possible

by relatively cheap train transport from the growing suburbs, and beyond, into the heart of the cities.

Paddington Station and its surrounding townscape have seen many changes since it was planned and built. What Brunel's station buildings mean to us today is conditioned as much by our sense of their past as by their everyday function; and it is to his credit that they have, almost without notice, become living history.

No engineer today would be able to exercise the single-handed control that Brunel had on every aspect of the Great Western speculative adventure.

Brunel's legacy endures – in the three-dimensional fabric of his buildings and in the vision of the engineering drawings – to show what imagination and determination could achieve.

The best Brunel could have hoped for, as an engineer, was that Paddington would still work as a railway station almost 150 years later. And it does.

PROJECT ASSESSMENT

Nicholas Grimshaw

For me, Paddington has always been an inspiration. I started using the station regularly when we got our first project in Bath in the early seventies, and I have often wondered about its almost universal appeal. The first thing one is struck by is its sheer scale. Until recently this was subtly revealed when driving into the station by the taxi ramp from the country end. The ramp is still there but no longer usable by taxis.

There is no doubt that railway stations were the cathedrals of the nineteenth century, but even so, Paddington seems to hold a special place amongst them. It was one of the earliest, being completed in 1855, pre-dating St Pancras by twelve years and Liverpool Street by twenty years. However, I think one of the most

significant things about its design was that it was a genuine collaborative effort between engineer, architect and fabricator. The idea of architects and engineers working together is much talked about nowadays, but at that time this was an innovative concept.

We can see from Brunel's letter to Matthew Digby Wyatt (quoted in the previous chapter) that he wanted involvement from the beginning. The letter continues:

> Now, in this building which, *entre nous,* will be one of the largest of its class, I want to carry out, strictly and fully, all those correct notions of the use of metal which I believe you and I share (except that I should carry them still farther than you) and I think it will be a nice opportunity.

He also secured the interest of Fox & Henderson who had been pivotal in

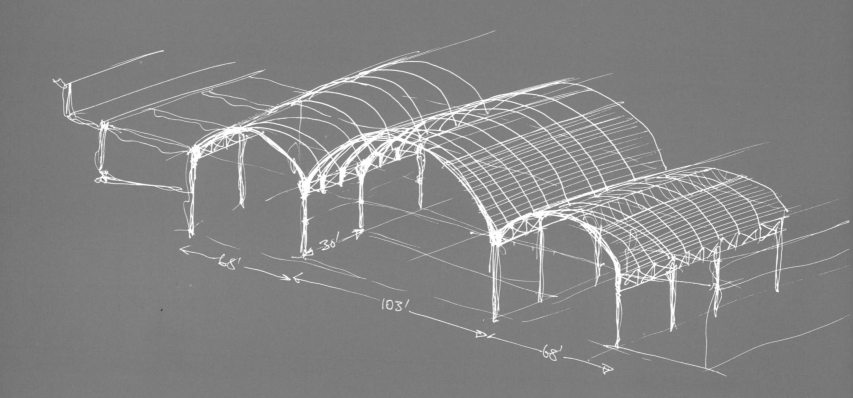

the detailing, mass production and fabrication of the Crystal Palace at a very early phase. The stage was therefore set for a wonderfully integrated design from the outset. It seems likely that Brunel set out the original ground plan of the arrangement of the 7 × 6 × 7 structural bays, with two transepts between each group of seven bays. Having two transepts at third points lengthwise, clearly distinguished the station from the traditional cathedral with only one.

However, what could have moved Brunel to have one grand central span of 102ft supported by a lesser span each side of 68ft, if it was not the cathedral concept of a generous nave with two side aisles? Certainly there seemed to be no particular reason for the spans arising from the track layout. This consisted of a grand Departure Platform, so poignantly shown in Frith's painting *The Railway Station*. This adjoined the main station building on Eastbourne Terrace.

The main arrival platform was in the 'third span'. Most of the central span was taken up with tracks leading to turntables at the end of the platforms so that carriages could be sorted and assembled into trains.

Looking at the structural concept as a whole it could not be more simple and spare. Lateral stability was achieved by using the main station building along Eastbourne Terrace on the south side, and propping through to the road embankment on the north side.

Longitudinal stability was achieved neatly and sparingly by cross-bracing as a kind of lacing between the arches, as well

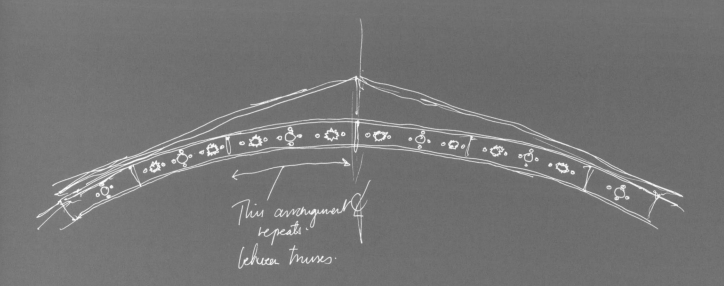

This arrangement
repeats.
between trusses.

as by very substantial and well-expressed wrought iron bracing between the column heads.

Turning to the details, one of the most immediately striking, is that there are two 'floating' arches between each column. These are elegantly and efficiently supported by the cross-bracing between the column heads – although this must produce three of the most stressed members in the whole station! Interestingly the 'bosses' under the ends of these arches are totally non-functional and mocked up out of timber. They nevertheless seem a fitting visual termination of these hard working spans.

Why are these arches only ten feet apart? It seems likely that, from his ship building experience, Brunel knew he could create slender, but immensely broad spans, using wrought iron ribs (an intuitive example of Victorian transfer technology). Additionally Brunel knew he could dispense with purlins and be one of the

first to use 'corrugated iron' as a structural spanning material.

Turning to the columns themselves, it is fascinating to note how slender the originals were, compared with their 1920s replacements. There are now only one or two Victorian columns at the extreme country end which remain as a testament to Brunel's original economy of structure. Nonetheless, the replacement columns, with their knobbly rivets joining together the obtuse angled segments, do have a certain style, and the echoing of the original column head detailing has been deftly done.

However, it is at the original column head that we see the close collaboration between Brunel, Digby Wyatt and Fox & Henderson. Not only does the column head show the forces coming on to it in a most expressive way, but Fox & Henderson's drawings of it have a richness and intensity worthy of any full-size computer generated detail of today.

Flowing from these column heads are the arches themselves, which in many ways are the true triumph of Paddington. Nobody can be sure whether Digby Wyatt's original cast iron decoration played a serious structural role in stiffening the ends of the arches as they landed on the columns. It depends on how they were originally fixed. However, there is no doubt that the way they deposit the forces in a petal-like, Art Nouveau form, strike most architects and engineers as profoundly satisfying. This embellishment, and the holes cut in the arches themselves, seem to symbolise a rare understanding between architect and engineer.

Digby Wyatt's strong design influence can also be seen in the huge castings which make up the platform frontage of the main station building. These are rich in detail but also play an important cross-bracing role in the structure.

Perhaps the most flamboyant aspect of Digby Wyatt's involvement can be seen in the huge scroll-like motifs laid over the end glazing of the arches. These too, seem in perfect organic harmony with the station design, whilst expressing the need for some kind of wind-bracing to support the end glazing.

Fox & Henderson's early drawings show a sparse station stripped of detail and it is fascinating to speculate how and when the detail was added. There can be no doubt that nothing was added which escaped the penetrating eye of Isambard Kingdom Brunel. Everything points to the idea that he whole-heartedly approved of this collaborative venture.

5 A TURKISH PREFAB
THE RENKIOI HOSPITAL

Eric Kentley

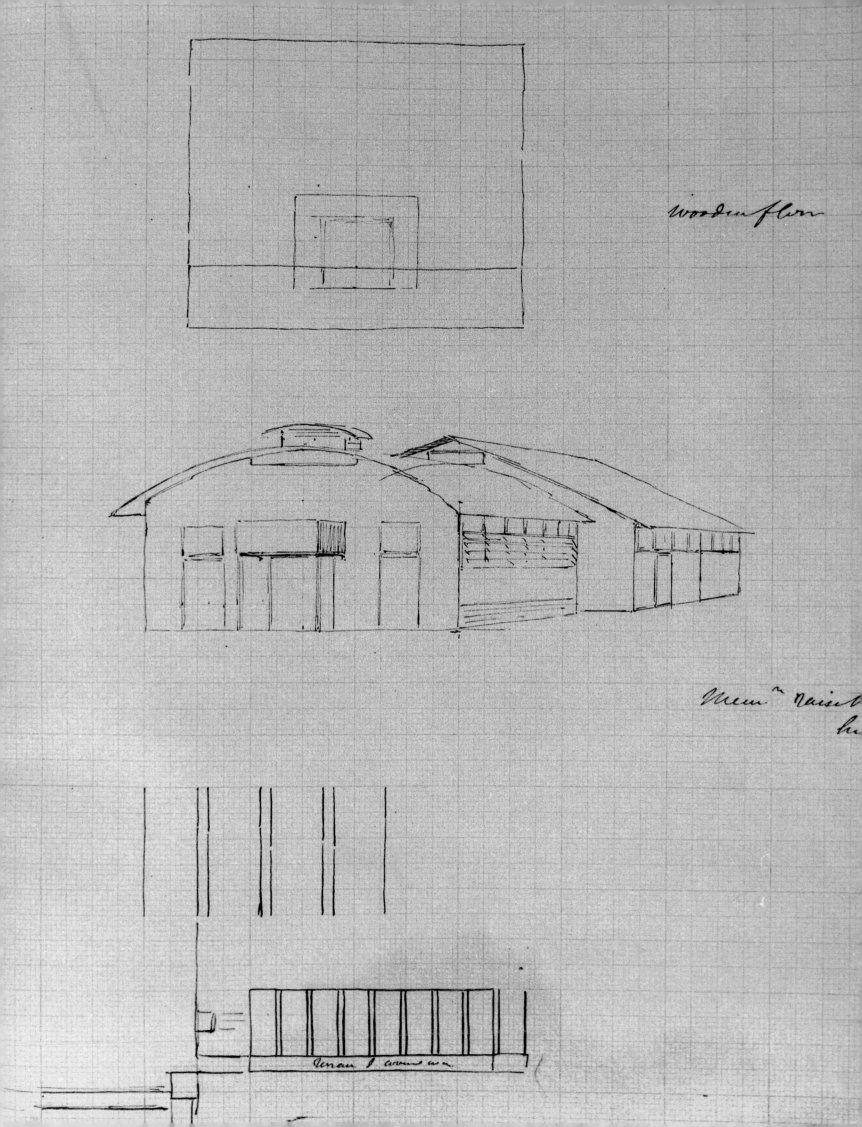

Wooden floor

Mem^n Maison
he

Unan I coming one

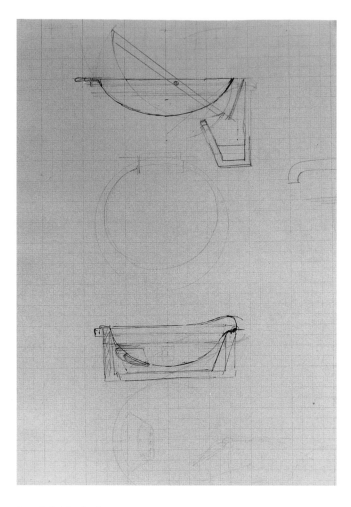

Brunel's sketches for the hospital's pivoting wash basins. *Bristol University Library*

Previous page
Brunel's sketches of the hospital buildings. *Bristol University Library*

HE TWO MOST SIGNIFICANT industrial buildings of the nineteenth century – according to engineer Derrick Beckett – were Paxton's Crystal Palace and Brunel's Renkioi Hospital. For they incorporated on a large scale the essential features of industrialised building – that is, the transfer of the focal point of the building process from the site to the factory.

The Crystal Palace to some extent lives on in the architecture of Paddington Station, and, indeed, is part of English folk memory. But Brunel's Renkioi hospital, built for the Crimean War and an early example of a pre-fabricated building, is forgotten. Yet the latter was a remarkable achievement. It was designed in 1855 – built, shipped and erected in Turkey, and ready to accept patients – all within five months.

It might have lacked the technological flair of the Crystal Palace or the Royal Albert Bridge, but it does reveal how Brunel could develop simple, economic and appropriate solutions to a whole range of problems. Little in the design was truly original; but, characteristically for Brunel, it was the ingenious combination of parts, and the thought put into materials, environmental management, servicing and assembly, that made the hospital a great – and successful – building.

War with Russia had begun in March of 1854. Fought by a creaking and inefficient British army, the war's most famous incident (one among a catalogue of blunders) was the disastrous Charge of the Light Brigade, and the war's

greatest hero was not a warrior but a nurse – Florence Nightingale – and for very good reason. The great scandals of the war were the horrific loss of life (34,000 troops out of a total of 56,000 died between September 1854 and January 1855) and the conditions of the sick and wounded.

Of the 22,000 survivors over 10,000 were in hospitals. These hospitals were overcrowded, understaffed and unheated. Dysentery, cholera and typhoid were rife, killing more than the battlefield.

As news came through – initially through the reports of the pioneer war correspondent W. H. Russell in *The Times* – Nightingale was given permission to take her nurses to the hospital in the former barracks at Scutari, across the Bosphoros from Constantinople.

The condition of the troops became a national scandal, precipitating the fall at the end of January of Lord Aberdeen's administration. But the establishment of the new government under Palmerston had little effect on the civil servants – such as the Permanent Undersecretary at the War Office, a person described by Nightingale as

… a dictator, an autocrat irresponsible to Parliament, quite unassailable from any quarter, immovable in the midst of a so-called constitutional government, and under a Secretary of State who is responsible to Parliament.

This bureaucratic monster who opposed the reforms of the army medical services to which Nightingale was so devoted, was none other than Sir

A TURKISH PREFAB

Benjamin Hawes, Brunel's best friend and husband of his sister Sophia.

At this time, Brunel was at the height of his career. Paddington Station was open, the Royal Albert Bridge was designed and about to be built, and the first plates of the *Great Eastern* had been laid. On 1 February 1855, the world's first postal train had run from London to Bristol along his Great Western Railway.

He was, nevertheless, far from oblivious to the events in the Crimea. In September 1854 he had designed floating gun carriages for attacks on the Baltic forts, although the Admiralty delayed even considering them until the war was over.

However, on 16 February 1855, the War Office invited Brunel to design a hospital for the British troops in the Crimea. No site was specified: a temporary hospital, capable of being erected on any reasonable piece of ground, which could be pre-fabricated in England and erected in the Crimea was required. Brunel replied on the same day:

This is a matter in which I think I ought to be able to be useful and therefore I need hardly say that my time and best exertions without any limitations are entirely at the service of the Government.

Such a swift and confident response almost certainly indicates that Hawes and Brunel had already discussed the project at some length, especially as within just six days, Brunel placed an initial contract for the supply of buildings for a 1,000-bed hospital.

This was highly irregular to the War Office Contracts Department, but Brunel knew speed was essential:

Such a course may possibly be unusual in the execution of government work, but it involves only an amount of responsibility which men in my profession are accustomed to take ... It is only by the prompt and independent actions of a single individual entrusted with such powers that expedition can be secured and vexatious and mischievous delays avoided ... These buildings, if wanted at all, must be wanted before they can possibly arrive.

By 5 March, Brunel was ready to present to the War Office. As he wrote to Hawes that day:

It is most gratifying to be able to state that from everybody I have received the most zealous and cordial assistance, and found it sufficient to mention the object of my enquiries to obtain immediately every assistance I could possibly require.

It is not known to whom he turned for advice. It is almost certain that it wasn't to Florence Nightingale, despite her detailed knowledge of the requirements of such a hospital. Her name is never mentioned in any of the correspondence between Brunel and Hawes relating to the hospital. L.T.C. Rolt speculates that the invitation may have been Hawes's attempt to show what he could achieve without the interference of 'that tiresome woman'. Nightingale, who never visited the resulting hospital, does, however, make a passing mention to the 'magnificent huts' in her *Notes on Hospitals*.

The idea behind the design was, 'that the several parts must be capable of being formed into a whole united by covered passages, and that it should be capable of extension by the addition of parts to any size.' An experimental ward was built at the Great Western Railway's premises at Paddington, which David Toppin, in his paper on the hospital,

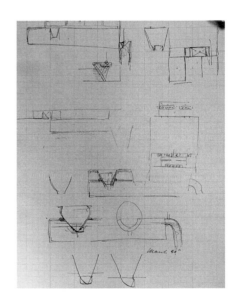

Brunel's sketches for the hospital's water closets. *Bristol University Library*

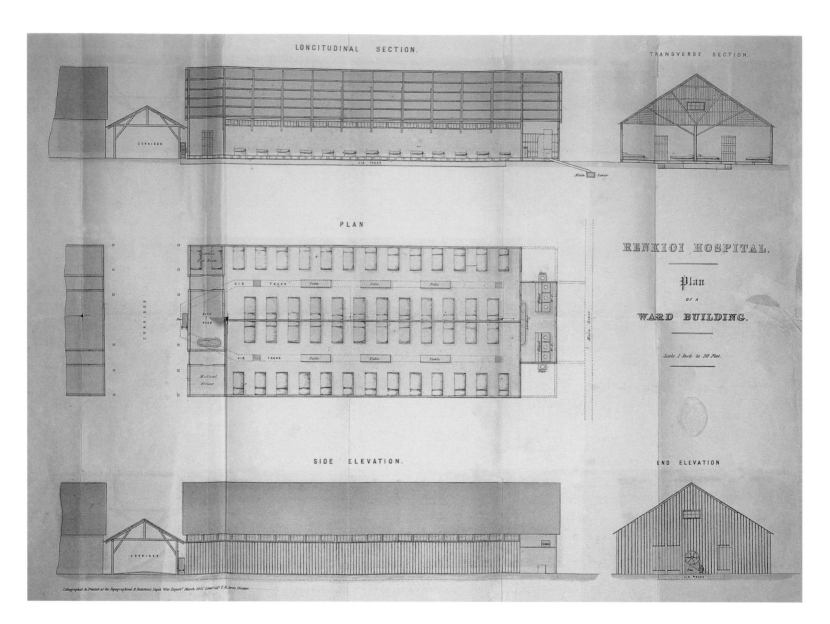

LONGITUDINAL SECTION.

TRANSVERSE SECTION.

PLAN

RENKIOI HOSPITAL.

Plan

OF A

WARD BUILDING.

Scale 1 Inch to 10 Feet.

SIDE ELEVATION.

END ELEVATION

Plan of a ward building
at the Renkioi Hospital by
Edmund Parkes, 1857.
*Wellcome Library,
London*

A TURKISH PREFAB

suggests would have allowed the performance of the heating and ventilation systems to be tested, as well as the structural strength and lightness of the structure. The work produced the only instance of a published account of a design written by Brunel himself, supposedly to satisfy the curiosity of his friends.

Despite its slightly repetitive and rambling style, this insight into Brunel's thinking justifies its quotation at length:

March 1855

The conditions that it was necessary to lay down in designing these buildings were:

Firstly. That they should be capable of adapting themselves to any plot of ground that might be selected, whatever its form, level, or inclination, within reasonable limits.

Secondly. That each set of buildings should be capable of being easily extended from one holding 500 patients to one of 1,000 or 1,500 patients or whatever might be the limit which sanitary or other conditions might prescribe.

Thirdly. That when erected they might be sure to contain every comfort which it would be possible under the circumstances to afford.

Fourthly. That they should be very portable and of the cheapest construction.

The mode in which it has been sought to comply with these conditions is as follows:

The whole hospital will consist of a number of separate buildings, each sufficiently large to admit of the most economical construction, but otherwise small and compact enough to be easily placed on ground with a considerable slope, without the necessity of placing the floor of any part below the level of the ground.

These separate buildings have been made all the same size and shape; so that with an indefinite length of open corridor to connect the various parts, they may be arranged in any form, to suit the levels and shape of the ground.

Each building, except those designed for stores and general purposes, is made to contain in itself all that is absolutely essential for an independent hospital ward-room; so that by lengthening of the corridors and the addition of any number of these buildings, the hospital may be extended to any degree.

To ensure the necessary comforts, and particularly to provide against the contingency of any cargo of materials not arriving on the spot in time, each building contains within itself two ward rooms, one nurse's room, small store room, bath room, surgery, water-closets, lavatories, and ventilating apparatus.

The ward-room is made wide enough and high enough to ensure a good space of air to each bed, even if these should be unduly crowded. Each building contains two ward-rooms, intended for twenty-six beds each, which is found in practice to be a size of room admitting of proper control and supervision.

With respect to closets and lavatories, after examining and considering everything that has to be done, both in hospitals of the best description and poor-houses of the cheapest construction, it was found that the requisite security for cleanliness and the greatest amount of economy of labour and of consumption of water, could be obtained by a cheap description of water-closet designed for the purpose; and with the same object of diminishing the amount of labour and waste of water, and securing cleanliness without depending upon the constant attention of assistants, fixed basins for lavatories and mechanical appliances for supplying and drawing off water were adopted.

As a protection against heat, experience in hot climates and experiments made expressly for the purpose satisfactorily proved that a covering of extremely thin and highly polished tin, which reflects all direct rays of heat, was the cheapest, lightest, and most effective protection, and every piece of woodwork not covered with tin is to be whitewashed externally. Internally the lime-wash has a slight tint of colour, to take off the glare.

To secure ventilation in a hot climate with low buildings extending over a large area, and therefore incapable of being connected with any general system of ventilation, it was considered that *forcing in* fresh air by a small mechanical apparatus attached to each building would be the only effective means. Each ward-room is therefore furnished with a small fan or rotary air pump, which, easily worked by one man, is found capable of supplying 1,000 to 1,500 cubic feet of air per minute, or 20 to 30 feet for each patient. This air is conveyed along the centre of the floors of each ward-room, and rising up under foot boards placed under the tables, is found to flow over the floor to every part of the room.

Besides this mechanical supply of air, opening windows are provided along the whole length of the eaves, and spaces left immediately beneath the roof at the two gables, amply sufficient together to ventilate the rooms thoroughly if any breezes are stirring, without the help of the fan.

The light is admitted by a long range of narrow windows, immediately under the eaves, which protect them from the direct rays of the sun. These windows open, and are provided with shutters inside, which exclude the light but admit the air.

By forcing the air into the room, instead of drawing it out, the entrance of bad air from the closets, drains or any other nuisances, is prevented. The fan is placed at the opposite end to the closets and drains; and all the fans being in the open corridor, the workmen can be seen by a single sentry, and kept to their work.

The buildings, as now constructed, are adapted to protect the interior from external heat. Should winter come while they are still in use, the framework is adapted to receive an internal lining of boarding, and the interstices can be filled with a non-conductor.

Two buildings of the same form and dimensions, are fitted up with every convenience as store-rooms and apothecaries' dispensaries.

An iron kitchen, slightly detached from the wooden buildings, fitted up with every contrivance capable of cooking for from 500 to 1,000 patients, is attached.

A similar building of iron is fitted up with all the machinery lately introduced in the baths and washhouses of London for washing and drying in the minimum space, and with the least labour.

If an aggregate of buildings should be placed in one spot for more than 1,000 patients, a second kitchen would be added, but the single washhouse would be sufficient.

With each set of buildings is sent a pumping apparatus, with a small reservoir, and a sufficient length of main, with all its branches, to supply water to every detached building; and all the pipes and branches are of such construction to admit of being put together without any soldering or cement. A system of drains is provided, formed of wooden trunks properly prepared, and of sufficient extent to form a complete and perfect system of drainage from every building to a safe distance from the general hospital.

A number of small buildings, intended to be detached from the main body, are provided for residences for the officers and servants of the soldiers. A slaughter-house and a store-yard and some other appurtenances are also provided, the extent of which depends on the circumstances of each case.

The construction of each building has been studied with great care, so as to secure the minimum amount of material, the least possible amount of work in construction or erection, and the means of arranging all the parts in separate packages capable each of being carried by two men; and the result is that each building is the cheapest and lightest that has yet been constructed in proportion to the area covered.

For the transport of materials to the spot selected, two sailing vessels and three steam-boats, capable of carrying one hospital for 1,000 men, which is the first about to be sent out, have been secured. In each vessel is sent a certain number of complete buildings, with every detail, including their proportion of water pipes and drains, closets, lavatories, baths, etc., and a small amount of surplus material and tools; and in each of two separate vessels are sent a set of pumps and mains and a kitchen and washhouse. So that by no accident, mistake or confusion short of the loss of several of the ships, can there fail to be a certain amount of hospital accommodation provided with every comfort and essential.

The peculiar circumstances under which these establishments are likely to be placed have required not only peculiarities of construction, but these, in turn, have required numerous provisions and details specially designed for the case.

As all the buildings, except the kitchen and washhouse, are entirely constructed of wood, it is considered essential that no stove or fire-place of any description should be allowed, except in the iron buildings.; in these there is provision for an ample supply of hot water, but each ward-building is provided with a small boiler, heated by candles, which by experiment have been found amply sufficient for all that can be required. Candles are to be used exclusively for lighting, and lamps and lanterns have been constructed for the purpose.

A proper supply of fire-engines is provided and other precautionary measures are adopted against fire.

As the space in the wards is very liable to be encroached upon, and the beds crowded, portable baths have been designed, into which the more helpless patients can be lifted, and lowered, on a frame or sack, without requiring space for assistants to stand around, or with the bath placed only at the foot of the bed.

The kitchen and laundry have each required many special contrivances.

The instructions given to Mr Brunton, [the Brunel-appointed site-engineer] who has been sent out for the purpose of erecting these buildings, are, to commence by determining on his plan of arrangement to suit the peculiarities of the ground, and then to construct the complete system of drainage and to lay on the water supply before the buildings are rendered capable of receiving patients; and all the arrangements of the details are designed with the view of obtaining, as the first conditions, a perfect system of drainage, a good supply of water, free ventilation, and the most perfect cleanliness, quite independent of labour and of the continued attention of assistants; these conditions being assumed as essentials, preceding even the mere covering in of space and providing shelter for patients.

The cost of these buildings, delivered ready for shipment, will be 18*l*. to 22*l*. per bed, allowing 1,000 cubic feet of space in each ward-room to each bed. If pressing emergency should lead to the beds being placed closer, and fifty per cent more patients should be introduced, it is believed that the perfect system of ventilation which is secured would render these hospitals very superior to any now in use for the army.

Of the costs above named, about 12*l*. per bed is that due to the ward-rooms themselves, with all their conveniences attached, and the rest arises from the cost of the store-rooms, kitchen, machinery, residences, and appurtenances.

The cargo space required for their conveyance is about a ton and a half to a ton and three quarters measurement per bed.

This account shows the level of detail at which Brunel could operate. However, his sketchbooks go even further, with drawings of how tilting washbasins might operate.

Standardised, prefabricated buildings were not a new idea: they had begun to emerge in the 1830s. The principles of sanitary hospitals had been well expounded by Florence Nightingale. Indeed, few of the individual elements in the design were completely new. But, completely characteristically, Brunel took the best of the existing ideas, developed them and produced a combination that was startling, practical

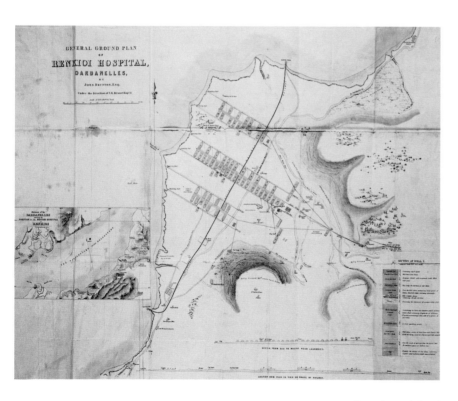

General ground plan of the Renkioi Hospital.
Wellcome Library, London

A TURKISH PREFAB

and successful. Toppin argues that it is the design concept that is as remarkable as the end product. It foreshadowed the idea of indeterminate buildings – that is, buildings whose use is not fully determined when they are designed and which are characterised by a linear organisational planning principle that builds in the potential for unknown growth.

It should not be forgotten that Brunel was an experienced and skilled designer in wood, as his trestle viaducts testified. Wood was clearly the most appropriate material for the hospital wards, not only for its lightness in shipping, but for its acoustic and thermal properties and its workability.

Brunel was not one to hand over his designs and leave their realisation to someone outside his control. He recommended John Brunton (whose father had once been in competition with him for the post of engineer of the Great Western Railway). Young Brunton was despatched to the Crimea at the end of March to find a site for the hospital. He went with the rank of Major and, as Hawes said, 'with greater powers than any other officer in Her Majesty's Army'. He was accompanied by a team of thirty men from the Army Works Corps, who would erect the buildings.

Nowhere suitable could be found on the Black Sea coast, so Brunton moved westwards towards the Dardenelles. Eventually, as he wrote in his memoirs:

I found a splendid site combining all my requirements as to natural formation, supply of water and freedom from malaria ... The village of Renkioi lay on top of the hills about two miles to the south west.

On 3 May 1855, Dr Edmund Parkes, a civilian doctor who had been appointed Medical Superintendent of the new hospital, and had seen Brunel's designs, visited the site and agreed with Brunton's proposal.

Brunel was not waiting idly at home for the site to be found. Rolt describes the letters he wrote to Brunton and Parkes as 'a classic example of that scrupulous attention to detail which was the secret of his success as an organiser'. Brunel had written to Brunton on 2 April:

All plans will be sent in duplicate ... By steamer *Hawk* or *Gertrude* I shall send a derrick and most of the tools, as each vessel sails you shall hear by post what is in her ... The son of the contractor goes with the head foreman, ten carpenters, the foreman of

From the road to Renkioi.
Private collection

Kitchen and hospital huts.
Private collection

the W.C. makers and two men who worked on the iron houses and can lay pipes. I am sending a small forge and two carpenter's benches, but you will need assistant carpenters and labourers, fifty to sixty in all… I shall have sent to you excellent assistants – try and succeed. <u>Do not let anything induce you to alter the general system and arrangement that I have laid down.</u>

To Parkes he wrote:

All the vessels with the entire hospital will I believe have left England before the end of next week, that is before 21st. Finding that none of the Ordnance Stores were likely to be ready, and indeed that no positive time could be ascertained for their being ready, I obtained authority yesterday to purchase one third of the required quantity of

bedding and some other similar stores and they are now going aboard with the buildings. I have added twenty shower baths, one for each ward and six vapour baths. You will be amazed to find also certain boxes of paper for the water closets – I find that at a cost of a few shillings per day an ample supply could be furnished and the mechanical success of the W.C.s will be much influenced by this. I hope you will succeed in getting it used and not abused. In order to assist in this important object I send out some printed notices or handbills to be stuck up, if you see no objection, in the closet room opposite each closet exhorting the men to use the apparatus properly and telling them how to do so. If you do not approve of such appeals the paper can be used for other purposes and perhaps impart some information in its exit from this upper world.

The buildings will be very quick after you; I almost fear you cannot have satisfied yourself about the site by the time they arrive. If you depend on Government Officers and if they at all resemble those at home, with one or two exceptions, your patience will be well tried.

In fact, the first consignment arrived just four days after the site had been agreed, and erection of the hospital began on 21 May 1855. This took longer than Brunel planned, but by 12 July the hospital was ready to receive 300 patients, by 11 August 500, and by 4 December the full 1,000. However, possibly because it was a civil hospital outside military control, the army procrastinated, and patients did not begin to arrive until 2 October, when 217 sick and wounded were brought ashore in one hour and twenty-five minutes. By January a horse-drawn railway had been laid to transfer patients the half mile from the pier to the hospital buildings.

The buildings withstood considerable winds, snowstorms and even earthquakes excellently. The only significant problem encountered was the leaking of the roofs on some of the buildings. However, it was to be short-lived. The Crimean War ended in January of 1856. By May most of the patients had been sent home and in July so were the remaining medical staff. Brunton was still there and was told by Brunel:

I don't want the thing to be flung into a ditch when done, but should prefer a useful end; that each part be made the most of and methodically and profitably be disposed of. Everybody here expresses themselves highly satisfied with everybody there and what we have done. I should wish to show that it was no spirit but just a sober exercise of common sense.

Having failed to persuade the Turkish government to buy it as it stood, the wards were sold off at a public auction on 20 September, some for housing homeless victims of a recent fire in Salonica. Brunton himself bought the water closets and lavatories, which he sold on to Netley Military Hospital, near Southampton, and the ventilating fans, which he sold on to the Admiralty.

Of the 1,331 military patients treated at the hospital in its short life, only 50 died: a 4 per cent fatality rate. The Scutari hospital's fatality rate was 42 per cent. Such statistics are used in both Rolt's and Vaughan's biographies as evidence of the success of the Renkioi hospital. However, as C. P. Silver points out, Scutari admitted 41,325 patients between June 1854 and June 1856. The largest number of patients at Renkioi at any one time was 642, and its position, a 72-hour journey from the Crimean Peninsula even by a non-stop steamer, meant that the majority of patients were convalescent rather than recently wounded or acutely sick.

This puts the significance of the Renkioi hospital into context. It takes nothing away from its design success. Parkes was unequivocal in his opinion from the outset:

I found that the formation of the hospital buildings, their size, shape, system of ventilation, water supply and drainage had already been considered and fixed by Mr Brunel, and that every arrangement was distinguished by that perfection of detail and excellence of method which stamps all the works of that distinguished engineer. I was convinced that nothing could exceed the excellence of the mechanical arrangements.

Brunel's triumph was not only in the design but also in the delivery of the project. It had taken just five months to design, transport, erect and open a completely new style of hospital. And, as Brunel's own words show, he controlled every detail, right down to the toilet paper.

Junior officers' quarters.
Private collection

The Renkioi engineer
John Brunton's hut.
Private collection

PROJECT ASSESSMENT

Jane Wernick

This project was remarkable not so much because of any spectacular structural innovation as for its appropriate and complete design, and for the speed and efficiency with which it was planned and built.

Brunel took the commission for a hospital that could be pre-fabricated in England, and built on almost any site with a relatively unskilled workforce, with characteristic enthusiasm and energy. He seems to have played the roles of architect; planner; structural engineer; mechanical engineer; public health officer and management contractor. He achieved the almost unbelievable task of taking the project from the initial inception of the idea to completion, including shipping, in a period of just five months. He received the commission on 16 February 1855 and by 12 July Renkioi was ready to accept 300 patients. By the end of March 1856 it could have accommodated 2,200 patients.

Brunel set out the key characteristics that were required of the design. What is notable is that he addressed all the requirements of a successful hospital: including not only the practical construction issues, but also those which would keep the patients healthy, ie good ventilation, sanitation, drainage and temperature control.

Because of his lack of knowledge of the actual site, he developed an arrangement of buildings that could accommodate changes in level, and which could be added as required.

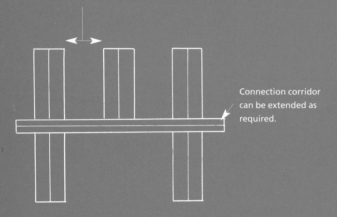

Gap between wards allows for good air circulation and can be carried to suit the terrain.

Connection corridor can be extended as required.

Brunel devised this linear arrangement of wards off a connecting corridor so that it could be adapted to any plot. Each ward is able to function independently.

Each unit links into the system of mains drains which are made of prepared wooden trunks. The main supply piping and branches can be connected without soldering or cement. Each set of buildings has its own pumping apparatus and small reservoir. The drainage trunks are long enough to drain a fair distance from the hospital.

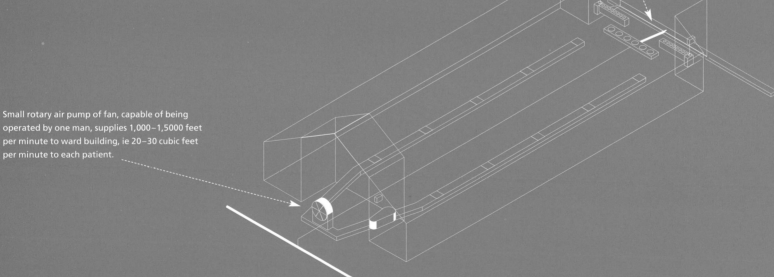

Small rotary air pump of fan, capable of being operated by one man, supplies 1,000–1,5000 feet per minute to ward building, ie 20–30 cubic feet per minute to each patient.

A TURKISH PREFAB

Openable windows at eaves and gable ends allow ventilation without the fan when there are breezes.

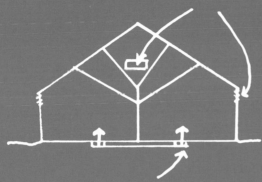

Humidity is added to the hot, dry air, by drawing it in over the reservoir. This also helps to cool the air.

Supply of air from pump from under floor, which forces air into the building and stops foul air from drains etc from entering building.

To minimise heat gains, the roofs are clad with thin, highly polished, reflective tin. All other external woodwork is whitewashed.

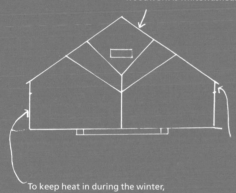

Long, narrow windows under the eaves, let in daylight but not direct sunlight. The internal limewash is tinted to take off the glare. Special lamps are used for the candles which provide heat and light.

To keep heat in during the winter, the walls are insulated between the external cladding and internal boards. A small boiler is provided for each ward building.

His proposal – for a linear, covered street or corridor, with standard ward buildings, and other units such as the soldiers' huts and the accommodation huts – provided flexibility and became a model for other indeterminate projects. His pragmatic approach led to a design which was able to be built quickly and which provided a hospital which finally admitted and treated 1,408 patients, with the total number of deaths being 50. This compared with a death rate of 42% that had occurred over the previous winter, as a result of the state of the existing buildings, which lacked sanitary provisions and were overcrowded and understaffed.

As well as the design and planning features, the success of this project was largely due to Brunel's ability to see clearly what had to be done, and then to set about getting the right people to do it, without regard for existing conventions or politics.

Each hospital ward building designed to contain
– 2 wards with 25 beds in each
– 1 nurses' room
– small store room
– bathroom
– surgery
– WCs, lavatories

The buildings are constructed in timber. The design was developed with the following aims:
– minimise the amount of timber used
– minimise the amount of effort required for construction
– design all packages so they are capable of being carried by two men

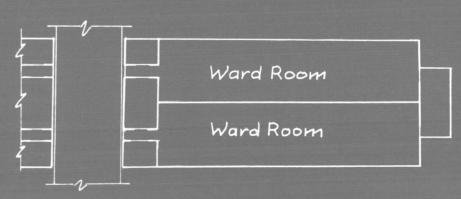

THE RENKIOI HOSPITAL

6 THE FINAL BRIDGE
THE DESIGN OF THE ROYAL ALBERT BRIDGE AT SALTASH

John Binding

Previous page:
The broad gauge track
on the bridge.
Stephen Rowson

ON 4 JULY 1844, the South Devon Railway Bill received the Royal Assent, and within five years the spreading network of lines across the country had reached Plymouth. To extend the railway into Cornwall, however, posed the problem of bridging the River Tamar. The Great Western Railway and the other broad gauge companies (the Associated Companies) had made their financial support for a railway in Cornwall conditional on the line forming an extension of the South Devon from Plymouth, and this involved a crossing of the Tamar estuary at one of its widest points – the Hamoaze.

Back in 1835, a scheme had been proposed for a railway line to run from Exeter to Falmouth via Okehampton and Launceston – thus bypassing Plymouth and crossing the river at its upper and narrower reaches. Although initially rejected by parliament, it was later revived by the threat of the loss of steam packet services from Falmouth (which indeed happened in 1843). Captain W.S. Moorsom, an ex– army engineer with little experience of railway construction, completed a survey of the proposed route in 1841. However, in view of the promised support of the Cornwall Railway by the Associated Companies, Moorsom undertook a survey of this alternative, more southerly route, to bring the line from Falmouth into Plymouth, proposing to cross the Hamoaze by adapting the already established steam ferry at Torpoint.

The effect of these two proposals was the emergence of two rival companies –

The bridge over the River Wye at Chepstow (the prototype for Saltash) in 1868.
Public Record Office

the Cornwall & Devon Central Railway (supporting the central route via Okehampton) and the Cornwall Railway which, with the support of the Associated Companies, proposed the southerly, coastal route. The relevant Bill for this latter scheme was introduced into the House of Commons on 24 February 1845. Here Moorsom was closely cross-examined by the Commons Committee, particularly regarding the Hamoaze crossing. A further witness was called – I.K. Brunel, who, in view of their projected involvement, had been retained by the Associated Companies to approve the plans for the line. He too was closely questioned regarding the crossing. When asked 'Will you state generally whether you consider the plan for crossing the Hamoaze will succeed?' his reply was

forthright – 'I think so, or I should not have agreed in recommending it.'

One of the Committee's many concerns was the effect of wind and tide on the approach of the ferry to the shore – particularly the need 'to draw the boat up at right angles'. Questioned as to whether he was prepared to suggest how this would be done, he replied, 'No: I am prepared to say that I consider there is no difficulty in doing it.' Again, his response to questions about loading the trains onto the ferry was confident – it was 'a very easy and simple thing to do.' The carriages would be run on the boats in the same way as private carriages and removed in a similar manner; the procedure was simple and 'no longer time would be consumed here than two minutes.' This was no more than other lines took in breaking up trains and starting them afresh. Finally, a boat might easily be made to carry six carriages. While one may marvel at Brunel's optimism over what may seem anything but a simple operation, it does pose the question as to whether he had an ulterior motive in adopting this stance.

When the Committee of the House of Lords came to consider the Bill, the Hamoaze crossing was examined yet again. Called as a witness was J. M. Rendel, who had built floating bridges and steam ferries for the Hamoaze and the Tamar at Saltash. He knew from experience that when wind and tide were strong, the chains on these ferries formed an arc, so that their platforms were not square to the landing place. He judged there would be considerable difficulty in lining up the rails on the floating bridge with those on the landing place, particularly in a place with such a marked rise and fall of tide – up to eighteen feet at spring tides. His estimate was a delay of eight to twelve minutes while the train was uncoupled and loaded, rather than Brunel's two.

After considering further evidence from experts such as Joseph Locke and Brunel's friend Robert Stephenson – both of whom had supported the central line and not the coastal route – the Committee finally delivered its judgement on 19 July 1845.

The noble chairman intimated that the Committee were of the opinion that the construction of a railway from Plymouth to Falmouth '… would be of great public advantage.' However, without a further and more accurate survey in order to obtain more favourable gradients and curves and, if possible, to avoid the crossing of the Hamoaze, 'the Bill should not now be proceeded with'.

Six days later the directors and officers of all the Companies involved met at Paddington and resolved to carry out the Lords' recommendations. They turned to Brunel – and on 26 August 1845 he was appointed as the Cornwall Company's Engineer. His brief was 'carefully to survey the country for the purpose of recommending such improvements or alterations in the line of the railway as may seem to him expedient', with a view to introducing a new Bill in the next session of parliament. Although crossing the Hamoaze by a steam bridge was still an

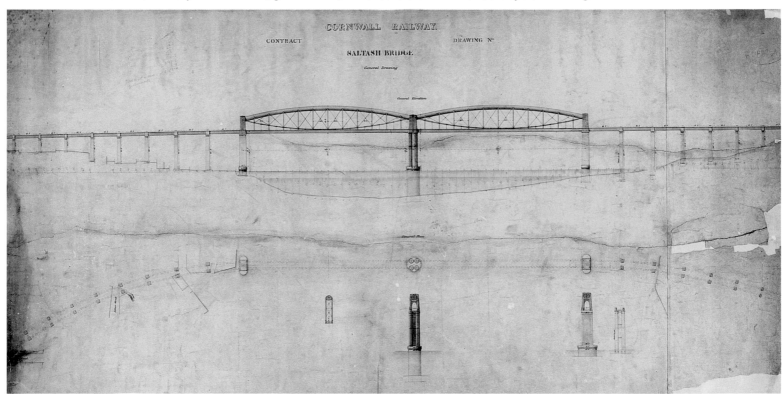

One of the contract drawings for the bridge.
Railtrack

option, Brunel was to investigate alternatives for bridging this 'Great Divide'. On 2 December 1845 he was advanced £2,500 for his work.

So far, Moorsom had conducted all the surveys, and, to avoid hurting his pride, Brunel suggested that he should assist in the new survey as and when required. In practice this collaboration proved unworkable and Brunel cancelled the arrangements at the end of the year.

There was still a real possibility of the line never being built, because of the continuing efforts of the central route supporters to bring their own line into favour. However, on 31 March 1846, their Bill was back before the House of Lords and, fortunately for the Cornwall Railway Company, it proved to be its swansong. The Bill was technically flawed – one report mentioned 'three thousand errors' – and was thrown out. This was the end of the Devon & Cornwall Central Railway Company. During the following year it was wound up.

Meanwhile Brunel worked on his survey. In general it followed Moorsom's original line, but using his own wider experience, Brunel made adjustments to the alignment in order to ease the curvature of the track and to keep gradients to a maximum of 1 in 60. Significantly, the survey proposed the building of a high-level bridge to carry the double-track line across the Tamar – two miles upstream from Moorsom's original crossing at Torpoint. Brunel's site was at Saltash where the river narrowed to 1,100ft with steep banks on both sides. From here, the line would follow the

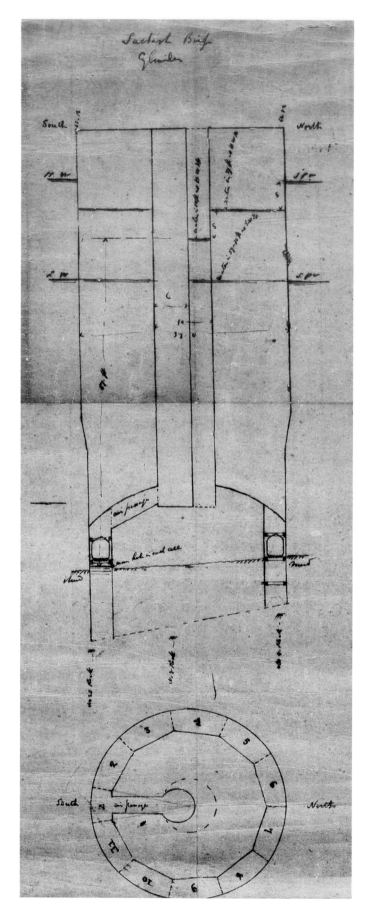

Brunel's concept for the great cylinder.
Railtrack

The great cylinder
being floated out.
Public Record Office

banks of the Hamoaze, inland from the dockyard at Devonport, and then swing south and east to reach the South Devon Railway terminus at Millbay. However, in submitting his plans for the overall route, Brunel maintained that:

the character of the county of Cornwall is such that no railway can be constructed at any moderate expense without either sacrificing all consideration for the interest of localities and the position of population to the mere choice of levels, or without steep gradients and sharp curves.

The revised Bill came before the House of Lords in June 1846. Again, Rendel submitted evidence, this time to argue that a bridge over the Tamar should be at least 100ft high. 'In the plans the crown of the arch appeared to be seventy and the rails eighty-two feet above high water', perhaps indicating that at that stage Brunel had in mind a massive single-arch bridge – probably in timber. Rendel estimated that a suspension bridge at Saltash would cost £83,000.

Brunel robustly defended his plans. His bridge would be ninety-five feet above mean high water mark, although it does seem that at this time he had not finally settled on a mode of crossing the Tamar that would be both practicable and affordable. But, given his reputation, the Committee seemed to have been prepared to accept the broad scope of his proposals and the Cornwall Railway Act received the Royal Assent on 3 August 1846. Among its many sections the Act specified that:

...the said Railway shall cross the River Tamar at Saltash by a Bridge to consist of Four Spans only, with straight soffits, all of which Spans shall be of such Dimensions, Height and Construction as shall be previously approved by the Lord High Admiral.

As the House of Lords Committee had ruled, the Admiralty, in the interests of navigation (that is, of tall masted sailing ships) had within their power to order the bridge to be of whatever height they pleased. However, if their demands could be satisfied, all the indications at that time seemed to be that the project could proceed speedily. Sadly, in the following autumn, shares in all railway enterprises slumped, with the value of even the most prestigious being halved. All new undertakings were shelved and the Cornwall Railway had no choice but to wait for better times.

It was Brunel himself who revived the plans in 1851, when he proposed that, instead of a double track, a single line should be laid from Plymouth to Falmouth, which would cost only £800,000, including the cost of the bridge at Saltash. Even so, it was another year before this proposal was accepted at the shareholders' meeting. Indeed, it was to be seventeen years from the passing of the Act, before trains finally reached Falmouth. The sixty-three miles of railway between Plymouth and Falmouth contained a number of major engineering feats, including 42 timber viaducts. Yet the most significant – and enduring – was the bridge across the Tamar at Saltash.

Brunel's first thoughts were to bridge the river by a single span of 225ft and six spans each of 105ft, set 70ft above high water mark. Their superstructures were to be formed as trussed arches in timber, probably supported on timber piles.

However, the proposals submitted to the House of Lords are capable of a variety of interpretations. While Brunel had at one stage considered a massive single span of 850ft, the Admiralty indicated their requirement to be two spans of 300ft and two of 200ft with straight soffits (undersides) and a clear headway of 100ft, which would have required three piers in deep water. Brunel's response was a design for a central pier in mid-stream with two spans of 465ft (later reduced to 455ft).

Preliminary investigations for the site of the central pier began in August 1847. Divers were unable to deliver sufficiently reliable information regarding the structure of the river bed. So in 1848, Brunel built a wrought iron cylinder (6ft in diameter and some 85ft in length) which was sunk into the river bed, to act as a coffer dam and enable trial borings to be made. Lack of money forced the suspension of the bulk of the preliminary work on the line in August of that year, but it was agreed that survey work for the central pier should be continued. Altogether, the cylinder was pitched at 35 different positions to make 175 borings over an area 50ft square, and from the data collected, a model of the rocky base was made to fix the precise location of the central pier. Yet, despite the success of this work and the positive results it produced, the lack of money persisted and nothing could proceed over the next three years, other than the preparation of drawings.

The Cornwall Railway was, of course, not Brunel's only project at this time. Amongst many others was the South Wales Railway, which entailed designing a bridge across the River Wye at Chepstow. Through his love of timber, his first thoughts had been to use timber trussed

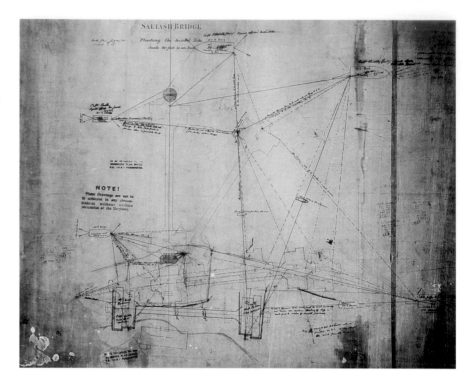

arches, but the Admiralty insisted on the bridge having a level soffit (giving 50ft clearance above high water over a width of 300ft), so he had to turn to alternative materials. In the meantime Robert Stephenson and his team, following their extensive investigation into the structural properties of wrought iron, were building the Conway Bridge (opened in 1848) and the Britannia Bridge (opened in 1850) in that material. Thus, with Stephenson's technical information available to him, Brunel chose wrought iron for Chepstow.

It has been said that not all of his earlier timber structures demonstrated a clear understanding of where the forces go, but his design for Chepstow showed a complete mastery of truss action when using iron. The overall design required a long embankment on one side and a

cutting into the hillside on the other, leaving 600ft to be bridged. Brunel divided this into a main river span of 300ft and three land spans each of 100ft, all fabricated from riveted wrought iron, incorporating two lines of broad gauge track, each carried on independent plate girderwork.

Each main span was in the form of a trapezoidal truss, supporting two longitudinal wrought iron girders, 72ft long, with top and bottom flanges of traditional Brunel design, which carried the trackwork. These girders were supported by 'suspension' chains, one set on each side of the roadway, hung from either side of an arched semi-horizontal circular tube. This was a substantial fabrication in wrought iron, with its ends resting on the tops of the main towers (which were located at each end of the span) about 50ft above the level of the rails. The 'land' tower was of masonry construction but the 'river' tower was of cast iron sections seated on the top of tubular piers. Two archways within each tower formed the portals through which the trains passed.

Within this formation, the tubes were in compression, with their respective roadway girders supported by the two sets of suspension chains; each of which comprised a series of 20ft long links, rolled as single pieces without welding of the eyes. Intermediate struts and diagonal wrought iron ties stiffened the centre panel of each truss and reduced the characteristic distortion of a suspended structure, introduced by a rolling load.

The land span girders for the trackwork were of similar design to those within the main span, and were thus continuous throughout the length of the bridge – reflecting the pioneer work carried out in 1849 by Brunel's assistant, Bell, into the behaviour of continuous beams.

The two main span tubes were raised into position ten months apart, so that the 'down' line was completed and operational by 14 July 1852 and the 'up' line by April of the following year. It is interesting to note that the cost of the Chepstow Bridge, with a nominal span of 600ft was £77,000, compared with £145,190 for Stephenson's 400ft Conway Bridge – statistics which would seem to contradict those who often unfairly

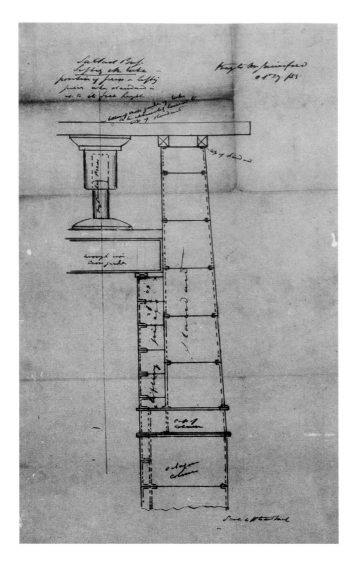

Copy of a working drawing showing the lifting of the tube at the centre pier to its final height. It shows the location of the temporary supports for the cross girder carrying the hydraulic press.
Railtrack

criticised Brunel for his expensive ideas.

The Chepstow Bridge was, in several respects, a trial run for his Saltash proposals. By 1849, with the experience of this crossing behind him, Brunel had largely settled the broad principles of his design – although the reduction to a single track was not formally agreed with the Board of Trade until 1852.

It is believed that the relevant calculations were carried out in his offices at 18 Duke St, but, sadly, apart from outline calculations in his notebooks of the early 1850s, the detail work does not appear to have survived. By 27 October 1852, Brunel reported to the Board that, apart from some details relating to the masonry, the drawings and specifications for the Saltash Bridge were ready.

Brunel's proposal was for each of the two main spans to be in the form of a Bowstring Suspension Bridge, made up of a wrought iron tubular arch or bow, with a profile generally in the form of a parabola, and with sets of suspension chains hanging on each side of the tube in a catenary curve. The rise of the tube was as great as the dip of the chains. The plate girder roadway was slung below the tube from eleven pairs of vertical members, or 'standards', passing through and connected to the chains. In addition, hangers located midway between each of these verticals were attached to the chains.

There is a tendency in a conventional suspension bridge for the chains to change shape under the influence of a train moving across the structure. This was overcome by restraining the movement of the verticals by a system of continuous diagonal bracing (comprising long wrought iron members connecting the tube to the chain) while each pair of verticals was braced by transverse struts and sets of diagonal stays.

Whereas the tubes on the Chepstow Bridge were circular in cross section, Brunel decided on an elliptical cross section for the Saltash tubes, 16¾ft in width and 12¼ ft in height. This not only gave greater lateral stiffness, but also allowed the suspension chains and bracing to hang vertically from the sides. In addition, this shape offered less wind resistance, although this factor does not appear to have been given significant consideration. The fabrication of each main tube incorporated substantial local strengthening at the points of greatest strain, in combination with a series of transverse and longitudinal internal stiffeners, while the ends themselves were closed off. However, to prevent the build up of condensation, 2in diameter drainage holes were drilled along the underside of each tube.

The distance between the two sets of suspension chains on each span was set at 16¾ft, the same as the width of the tube. In turn, each set of main chains was made up of two formations of links. Where their ends connected to the tube, the latter was substantially reinforced to form four spaces into which the chain links were grouped to fit, and secured by massive wrought iron bolts. The bolts were staggered and consequently the upper chain of each set had to be approximately one foot longer than the lower.

Thus, each main chain was formed of two groups of wrought iron links, spaced one above the other at approximately 14in centres. Each tier comprised a combination of either 14 links or 15 links, side by side in alternate panels, each set weighing approximately 3 tons. These links were 7in deep with their ends enlarged to accommodate a 4⅛in-diameter hole at 20ft centres to suit a 4in diameter wrought iron pin, which thus connected the interlaced links.

Some of the links, incorporating a welded eye, had been made in 1843 for the Clifton Suspension Bridge – one of Brunel's earliest projects which unfortunately, through lack of finance, could not be completed in his lifetime – and were purchased for Saltash. The remaining links were manufactured in 1857 to include an integral forged eye.

The roadway was designed with a rise of three feet from each end to the central pier, incorporating a smooth camber. The supporting girders were 8ft deep and incorporated Brunel's typical half round upper flanges. As described above, these girders were suspended from the chains through a series of 'standards' while between each standard was an intermediate suspension link, having its upper end attached to the chains and its lower end to the flange of the roadway girder. Fabricated cross girders seated on the lower flange of the main girders, supported timber decking, which carried the ballast and permanent way.

The points where the 'standards' were intersected by the chains were braced to the main tube by diagonal wrought iron

ties. The main connecting pins of this linkage were apparently made about 4⅛in smaller than the holes in which they fitted – a lapse from good engineering practice that was to prove troublesome in service. In addition to this diagonal bracing, each pair of standards also incorporated transverse bracing and diagonal stays.

On both foreshores, a massive granite pier supported the end of each main span, 130ft from foundation to the level of the rails. Above this, portals of stone and brickwork, encased in cast iron shrouds, neatly concealed the ends of the massive overhead tubes and the ends of the roadway girders.

The base of the centre pier was a circular column of masonry, 35ft in diameter and rising 96ft from the bedrock to 12ft above high water mark. On its

upper surface two pairs of octagonal cast iron columns set in a square, were built up from 6ft sections, flanged and bolted together, extending to a height of 88¾ft at rail level. Transverse cast iron bracing linked the columns of each pair but there was no longitudinal bracing between the pairs. At their tops was the central portal, formed from four massive cast iron frameworks, similar in construction to the columns. This portal incorporated the location which supported the end of each tube, and thus provided their fixed centre bearing. A cast iron shroud covered in the ends of the tubes and chains.

The ends of the spans were placed on a series of rollers on the landward piers. This allowed them to slide in and out, as (with changes in temperature) they expanded and contracted.

After completion the bridge was rigorously tested. This drawing shows the extent of the deflections of each span under various test loads. *Railtrack*

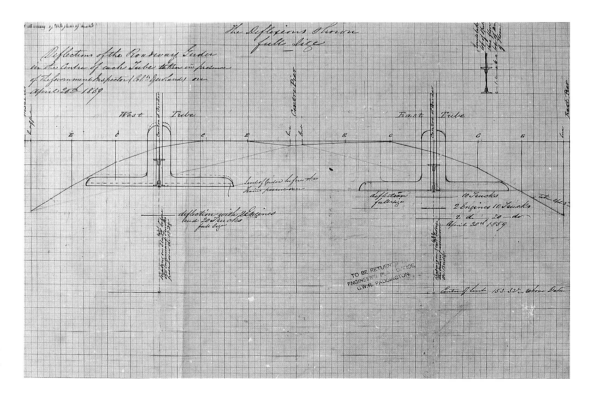

The completed bridge, late nineteenth century. *Railtrack*

The approach spans from each shore are supported on double columns of solid masonry. Initially formed from wrought iron plate girders, generally similar to the main bridge girders, the 17 spans are not uniform in length – they are arranged to be shorter the further they are away from the centre of the river, such an arrangement believed to be an aesthetic decision by Brunel. Overall the length of the structure is nearly 2,200ft. Having regard to the sharp curvature of these spans and its general construction, a speed limit of 15 mph has always applied for trains crossing the Bridge.

Brunel was paid £5,000 for his design - more than £250,000 in today's value – which he took in the form of 308 shares in the Cornwall Company. He also received further sums for expenses and the salaries of his assistants and surveyors.

Even before the completion of the final design work, the fortunes of the Cornwall Railway Company were improving and Brunel had tenders for the work ready for the Board by the middle of January 1853. Following their due consideration, the contract was awarded to C.J. Mare, the Blackwall ship builder, who had been the principal contractor for Stephenson's Menai Straits Bridge, completed in 1850. On the Devon foreshore he immediately set up the facilities necessary for the work involved, the sheds and yard to be known as 'Saltash Bridge Works'.

Undoubtedly an expert in wrought iron fabrications, Mare was less experienced with regard to the techniques involved in the foundation work for the centre pier, and the delays and frustrations in this aspect of the contract led to his eventual bankruptcy in 1855. Brunel had devised the method for its construction based on the use of a wrought iron cylinder, 37ft in diameter, sunk onto the riverbed, within which the foundations were to be constructed. The many difficulties encountered during this time, delayed completion of the massive granite centre pier to November 1856.

Meanwhile, construction of the first main span was proceeding on the Devon foreshore and on completion, following a significant static test. Brunel arranged to have this floated out on 1 September 1857, and set between the bases of the centre and land piers on the Cornish side. This tricky operation, involving coordination of movements ashore and afloat involving some 500 men, was safely completed. Once in position it was progressively raised using hydraulic jacks, with the masonry and cast iron supports being built under the ends, until it reached its final position by May 1858. Work had been started on the Devon span, which was floated out on 10 July 1858 and finally reached its full height by the end of the year.

With the area of the foreshore thus cleared, the piers for the Devon approach spans could be completed and positioned, so that the Bridge was ready to receive its first train in April 1859.

There followed a period of inspection by the Board of Trade, carried out by Col W. Yolland CB FRS, a man of enormous prescience and immense influence on the development of railway safety during his time with the Railway Inspectorate. Over a period of three days he conducted a rigorous series of tests on the Bridge, the outcomes of which were 'highly satisfactory' and the structure was passed for service some six years from the date of contract.

The Cornwall Railway and the Royal Albert Bridge were formally opened on 2 May 1859 when Prince Albert travelled down by train from Windsor to Saltash to perform the opening ceremony, an occasion of great pomp and circumstance appropriate for this marvel of the age. Sadly, Brunel was unable to be present: his deteriorating health kept him on the Continent and it was not until later in the month that he returned to England. Then, because of his impaired health, arrangements were made for him to visit Saltash to view his completed masterpiece from a couch fitted to a specially prepared platform truck, slowly drawn across the Bridge by one of Gooch's locomotives. He never recovered from his illness and he died later in the year.

As a tribute to his memory, and in recognition of his contribution to the construction of the Cornwall Railway and the Royal Albert Bridge in particular, the Directors arranged for the letters 'I K BRUNEL ENGINEER 1859' to be set on the portals at each end of the Bridge – a striking reminder today to travellers who cross the Tamar of the work of this great engineer.

In subsequent years as the bridge has continued to form the essential rail link between Devon and Cornwall, it has been subject to detail modifications to accommodate the increasing loads of contemporary traffic. These have included the change from broad gauge trackwork;

strengthening of the decking supports; replacement of the wrought iron approach spans by steel girders; and, in particular, the addition of extra bracing within the supporting framework to counter the effects on the structure of the later, heavier locomotives. A number of modifications have also been made to the connections to counter the effect of corrosion-fatigue.

The demise of the steam locomotive with its attendant 'hammer blow', and the introduction of welded trackwork, have contributed to the structure being able to carry the increased axle loading of the modern freight vehicle. A recent detailed survey of the bridge confirmed that, having regard to its age, it is generally in a sound condition to remain in service for a number of years to come.

Reviewing the position of a major engineering structure like the Royal Albert Bridge, still in daily use some 140 years after it was first completed, warrants special consideration of the factors affecting its original design. In 1845 Brunel had been charged with establishing a route for the Cornwall Railway to include bridging the River Tamar. At that time his friend and professional rival, Robert Stephenson, was faced with a commitment to build a massive bridge across the Menai Straits for the Chester & Holyhead Railway – in a very short time with no known method of meeting the requirement. Consultation with William Fairburn and Baton Hodgkinson resulted in the concept of a circular or elliptical tube with the trains running through it. From this, following

Installing the tribute to I.K.B. shortly after his death in September 1859.
Private collection

THE DESIGN OF THE ROYAL ALBERT BRIDGE AT SALTASH

THE FINAL BRIDGE

extensive testwork, the design developed to the final continuous box girder of rectangular section which proved to be such a structural success.

However, while their investigation established fundamental data regarding the strength of wrought iron, their obsession with carrying trains across the Straits in a wrought iron tube distracted their attention from consideration of the overall efficiency of the design, which in practice proved to be very expensive. Of its total cost of approximately £600,000, less than 1% was absorbed by the experiments that played such a critical role in making the bridge a structural success.

In his approach to the design of the Saltash Bridge, whilst he could simply have copied Stephenson's tubular solution, Brunel chose to adapt the results of Stephenson's testwork to his own concept of how to construct spans of 400–500ft. He evolved a design using large tubes as compression arches and wrought iron chains as suspension chains in a self-equilibrating arrangement that has been described as looking somewhat like a lenticular truss. In this he was developing the idea which he first incorporated in his bridge across the Wye at Chepstow.

Measured per foot of track length, the Saltash Bridge contained only 4,700lb of iron compared to the Britannia's 7,000lb while in terms of £ sterling per ft of single track, the cost of Saltash was only about half that of the Britannia crossing. These figures clearly illustrate the greater efficiency of Brunel's design:

while from an operational aspect, the open tube construction of Saltash was immensely superior to the long closed tube of Britannia. In practice, the sun could heat the latter's inside to unbearable temperatures, thus making the passage through it an uncomfortably warm experience.

Throughout his working life, Brunel, in his striving for perfection, tended to keep the details of his projects under his own close supervision, which often led to excessive costs as he introduced progressive modifications at will. The cost of some of his works did indeed attract criticism: but the comparison of his bridge design with Stephenson's, reflects his constant endeavour to achieve the optimum result – both structurally and economically.

His design for Saltash remains unique, being the only semi-suspension bridge in daily use on a main trunk railway. Although Brunel had no major precedent on which to base Saltash, he boldly used the state-of-the-art technology of the 1850s to achieve the most economic design.

The result is as good a solution as could be hoped for, and one which – with suitable modification over the years – has stood the test of time.

Royal Albert Bridge,
Saltash, 2000.
Andrew Cross

SALTASH BRIDGE V CLIFTON SUSPENSION BRIDGE

Tony Hunt

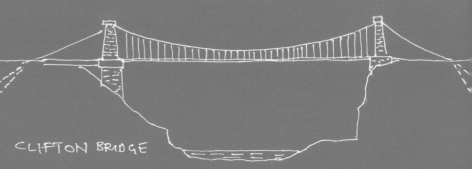

CLIFTON BRIDGE

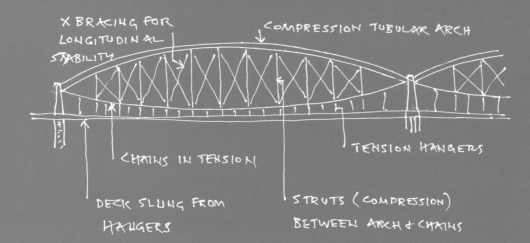

X BRACING FOR LONGITUDINAL STABILITY

COMPRESSION TUBULAR ARCH

CHAINS IN TENSION

TENSION HANGERS

DECK SLUNG FROM HANGERS

STRUTS (COMPRESSION) BETWEEN ARCH & CHAINS

Clifton Suspension Bridge is just that – a bridge with wrought iron tension chains suspended from hangers supported on stone arches. Its setting, high across the Avon Gorge, is undeniably spectacular. But Saltash Bridge is unique in its design and form of construction. It combines three classical engineering forms:

– the Compression Arch
– the Tension Chain
– the Beam Deck

The Principle – A Bowstring
The outward thrust of the Saltash Bridge arch is counteracted by tension chains, with struts holding the two elements apart.

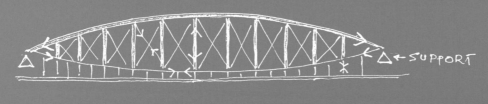

SUPPORT

 MEMBERS IN COMPRESSION

—— MEMBERS IN TENSION

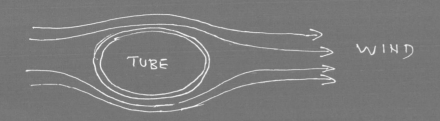

TUBE

WIND

CROSS SECTION AT MID SPAN

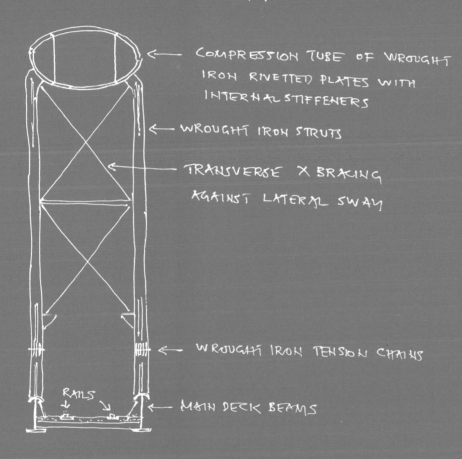

← COMPRESSION TUBE OF WROUGHT IRON RIVETTED PLATES WITH INTERNAL STIFFENERS

← WROUGHT IRON STRUTS

← TRANSVERSE X BRACING AGAINST LATERAL SWAY

← WROUGHT IRON TENSION CHAINS

RAILS

← MAIN DECK BEAMS

Prefabrication

The main spans, each 455ft (138.7m) long, were fully prefabricated on the shore, then floated on the river on pontoons and progressively jacked up the piers to their final position 100ft (30.5m) above water level.

Each complete span weighed in excess of 1,000 tons.

Saltash is, in effect, a suspension bridge where the deck is hung from chains. It is a rare type, using what is called a 'closed system' ie the forces are all contained within the structure.

Certainly in terms of railway bridges, Saltash is unique — and very clever.

The Compression Tube

The tube is oval in cross-section. This shape provides extra lateral (sideways) stiffness for wind loads and also allows smoother wind flow.

CLIFTON — OPEN

SALTASH — CLOSED

THE DESIGN OF THE ROYAL ALBERT BRIDGE AT SALTASH

7 BRUNEL AND THE SCREW PROPELLER

Andrew Lambert

ALTHOUGH BEST KNOWN as a 'builder' of railways and steamships, Isambard Kingdom Brunel was, first and foremost, a designer. The creative centre of his working life was the design process, where his superior technical and theoretical understanding enabled him to exploit the available materials and machines to their limit. Although inventive, Brunel was not primarily a creator of new systems. His talent was deployed to perfect what was available – often transforming the original ideas of others into something altogether more sophisticated. Nowhere was his design input more important than in the introduction of the marine screw propeller.

Brunel came to this task at the end of the 1830s, having established himself as the country's foremost engineer through his work on the Great Western Railway and the *Great Western* – the first effective Atlantic steamship. For Brunel, the development of the steamship was both a legacy from his father, and a test of his ability to translate an expanding world of engineering knowledge into a superior end-product. His design skills were tested to the limit by a system that operated in the most demanding environment of all – the sea.

He took no fee for his work on the ships and invested his own money in the Great Western Steamship Company. In the space of twenty years he would design the world's finest wooden paddle-wheel steamship by perfecting his father's pioneering effort; introduce new materials into every aspect of ship structure and design; and, by applying a new propeller system, create the modern ship.

When designing the *Great Western*, Brunel had wisely relied on proven technologies, the wooden ship and paddlewheel propulsion. Having successfully established his credentials and greatly enlarged his understanding of the problems, he was now well placed to integrate new systems in his second Atlantic liner.

By 1840, Brunel was ready to use an iron hull with a screw propeller – two critical technologies that would herald a new age. Brunel conceived the screw steamship as an integrated machine in which the ship, her structure, form and machinery, all combined to create a harmonious and efficient vessel with the screw propeller at its heart.

For all his innate talent, the key to Brunel's work was the unique, bi-lingual scientific, technical and engineering education provided by his father, Sir Marc Brunel – the finest designer of his generation.

After mastering mathematics in France, Isambard worked with Louis Breguet (the leading Parisian chronometer and scientific instrument maker) and completed his education in Henry Maudslay's Lambeth engineering works. Sir Marc also introduced Isambard to his circle of friends. These included scientists, patrons and liberal politicians – the most important member of the circle being Charles Babbage, the mathematician and pioneer of the mechanical analogue computer. Brunel's superior education

Charles Babbage,
c.1847.
National Portrait Gallery

enabled him to work with Babbage – Brunel's peculiar genius integrating the, then, largely separate worlds of science and engineering. He translated this talent into practical form through the medium of design.

The application of a screw to marine propulsion has a long and appropriately convoluted history. Before 1836, numerous engineers, speculators and theorists raised the subject. A few actually experimented (including Sir Marc) but none translated their ideas into practical form. This failure reflected the limited theoretical knowledge available, the lack of efficient steam machinery to drive the propeller, and also the lack of adequate funding to conduct full-scale trials. Most early propellers were highly inefficient, being conceived for very low engine speed operation.

The two men who brought the system into practical use, Francis Pettit Smith and John Ericsson, took out patents in 1836. They used gears to drive the propeller at higher speeds and both built functional screw-propelled boats. Ericsson, a trained engineer, designed a more effective screw than Smith, but he applied it in the wrong place. He also lacked the funds to develop it. Smith, an inspired amateur, managed to secure financial backing for his simple Archimedean screw, but he lacked the theoretical and engineering knowledge to develop it from functional system to finished design. His major development breakthroughs resulted from good fortune, rather than design. The technical limits of Smith and the Ship Propeller Company that supported his work, were revealed in their 200-ton test ship the *Archimedes*. Her poor systems integration and engineering flaws obscured the true merits of screw propulsion.

After initial trials in London and extensive testing by the Royal Navy, the *Archimedes* was sent around Britain to publicise the screw, arriving at Bristol in May 1840. This was timely, for Brunel was trying to improve the performance of the paddle wheels for the *Great Western* and a new ship then being built. On 18 June, Brunel advised the Directors of the Steamship Company to consider screw propulsion for their new ship. And after trying the *Archimedes* at sea, the Great Western Company's Building Committee sent their engineering consultant, Thomas Guppy, on the ship, when she steamed north to Liverpool. Guppy's report on the boisterous voyage persuaded the

Committee to suspend work on the stern of their iron paddle wheel ship while conducting further trials with *Archimedes*.

Despite the opposition of three key figures in the steamship project, Brunel persisted, experimenting on the *Archimedes* in the Company's workshops, gathering data on engine performance, transmission systems and sea-going capability. These were the first trials on a screw ship devised to exploit the existing theoretical and practical knowledge of ship propulsion.

Brunel used the data to produce a ground-breaking report, which he delivered to the Steamship Company in October 1840. This document 'marks the birth of the scientific approach to

propeller design'. In contrast to the screw pioneers, Brunel had made a scientific examination of ship propulsion. He combined data from pioneering hydrodynamic trials (which his father had used twenty-five years before) with a very full set of data on the propulsive efficiency of the *Great Western*. Others had conducted much of this work, and it was a mark of Brunel's approach that he delegated important experimental work to trusted subordinates.

Using full data sets for *Archimedes* and *Great Western,* Brunel compared the screw and paddle wheels as propellers. He then considered whether the advantages of the screw justified its adoption. He calculated that the *Archimedes* was efficiently propelled –

SS *Great Britain* alongside the Gas Works Wharf in Bristol, c. 1834, photographed by W.H. Fox Talbot.
National Maritime Museum 3758

even though the ship was of inferior form, the machinery of poor design, and the propeller roughly finished:

> As compared with the ordinary paddle wheel of sea-going steamers, the screw is, both as regards the effect produced, and the proportionate power required to obtain that effect, an efficient propeller.

Brunel then addressed the advantages of the system; reduced weight, a simpler hull form and:

> ... being unaffected by the trim or rolling of the vessel ... allowing of the free use of sails, with the capability of entirely disconnecting the screw or of varying the multiplying motion so as to adapt the power of the engine to the circumstances either of strong adverse winds or scudding.

This discussion reflected the particular circumstances of Atlantic passages under steam, where wind assistance was very welcome. The sail-assisted system he adopted for the *Great Britain* would be the most efficient installed for a century. The Royal Navy, with much larger crew, persisted with the old square rig. In addition, the screw avoided the constant succession of shocks as the paddleboards hit the water, shocks which often damaged the engines. Other benefits included improved steering, increased cargo capacity and a reduction in the ship's beam:

> My opinion is strong and decided in favour of the advantage of employing the screw in the new ship [the *Great Britain*] ... I am fully aware of the responsibility I take upon myself by giving this advice. But my conviction of the wisdom, I may almost say the necessity of our adopting the improvement I now recommend is too strong, and I feel it is too well founded, for me to hesitate or to shrink from the responsibility.

Although Brunel recognised *Archimedes* as an inefficient compromise, he had the vision to propose modifying the new transatlantic steamer (which he had already persuaded his colleagues to build in iron) into a screw vessel. Two days after submitting his report, Brunel told one of them that 'taking into consideration all the advantages of the screw it was better than any paddle and would soon supercede the paddle.'

The combination of the screw and the iron hull created the modern ship. Alone of all those who saw the *Archimedes*, Brunel recognised the fundamental advantages of the screw for full-powered ocean-going ships, and advocated a complete commitment to its use to propel the largest ship in the world. So persuasive was his advocacy that, despite the enormous financial and technical risks involved, the Building Committee accepted his report in December 1840.

After the *Archimedes* returned to London, Brunel advised Smith's Ship Propeller Company to continue his experimental work, notably on the frictional resistance of the screw, and suggested that the Royal Navy might support this work.

The Ship Propeller Company lost no time using Brunel's research to promote their system. Even before the Great Western Company adopted the screw, the Controller of the Royal Navy Steam Department, Captain Edward Parry, was anxious for reports on 'the large iron ship, including the <u>Screw</u>'.

In December, Brunel dined with Pettit Smith, while Parry requested an unofficial copy of his propeller report. Parry had already recommended building a replica of the paddle wheel sloop HMS

Propeller from HMS *Rattler*, preserved at Portsmouth.
Royal Naval Museum

On 3 April 1845, HM Steam Sloops, *Rattler* and *Alecto*, engaged in a tug-of-war to test the relative powers of the screw propeller and the paddle wheel. The propeller-driven *Rattler* won.
National Maritime Museum PY 0923

Polyphemus, suitably modified to test the screw. When Smith advised very substantial modifications to the ship's hull, Parry sought Brunel's opinion.

In mid-March 1841, Parry invited Brunel to direct the screw project, having sole charge of the mechanical arrangements and the experimental testing of the ship. The details were settled, although only verbally, at the Admiralty (the Board that directed the Royal Navy) on 27 April. Brunel quickly tested the *Polyphemus* to determine her resistance in proportion to her midship area – data that could be compared with figures obtained from *Archimedes*. He advised Parry that 'the construction of the vessel should, in the first instance, be made entirely subservient to the single object of making a full and complete experiment upon this system of propelling'. Once the system was proven, an integrated screw propeller ship could be designed. He stressed that one of the major advantages of the new system would 'undoubtedly be the facility it affords of carrying sail, either with or without the steam.'

In September 1841, Parry recommended that Brunel's role be enhanced to reflect the value of the work he had already carried out for the Admiralty and the Great Western Company, and the fact that he had no financial stake in the success of the screw. Brunel would be responsible for installing the machinery and propeller. Smith was confined to the design and location of the screw. This was a critical decision. While Smith was only concerned to prove the screw concept, Brunel's superior all-round engineering vision ensured that it would be taken to its limits.

In late September 1841, the introduction of the screw propeller into naval service was thrown into confusion by a change of government. As Brunel's relationship with the Admiralty had been a gentleman's agreement based on political friendships, the change came at a particularly unfortunate time. He would have to build anew the personal relationships that were essential to the smooth functioning of nineteenth century administration.

Throughout the second half of 1841, Thomas Guppy continued the Great Western's experimental work on the *Archimedes*. Brunel fed Guppy's results into his work for the Navy, hoping they would 'enable me to obviate some of the objections which I understand have been felt regards the construction of the vessel'. Called to a conference at the Admiralty late in 1841, he used the latest Bristol results to oppose the conversion of an existing paddle wheel vessel for the screw, stressing that the ship was of inferior form.

On 17 January 1842, Brunel reminded First Sea Lord Admiral Sir George Cockburn that the *Archimedes* had already demonstrated that the screw could do the same work as the paddle wheel. The new ship would determine:

> … whether all the advantages claimed by the promoters of the invention anticipate, of the vessel being capable of being constructed with perfect sailing qualities – and of a press of sail being advantageously carried, either with or without the working of the engines and without stopping to connect or disconnect, and of the efficient working of the screw in the heaviest sea.

To settle these questions, and to reach reliable conclusions about the relative efficiency of the screw and paddle wheels, it was essential to build a vessel with a form suitable for the screw. Any compromise would invalidate the experiment and it would have to be done again. Suitably persuaded, the Admiralty returned to the original plan, ordering a replica *Polyphemus*, named HMS *Rattler*, on 24 February 1842.

Brunel also persuaded the Admiralty that Maudslay, Sons & Field should design, manufacture and install the engines, boilers, shafting and all related metal fittings. This reflected both their eminence as marine engineers, and Brunel's friendship with managing partner, Joshua Field. An integrated engineering plant, built by the leading firm, minimised the risk of mechanical failure compromising the trial.

Brunel left Smith to design the propeller and decide if the screw should be fitted for unshipping without going into dock. This was an unusual oversight on his part, given that the vessel would be shifting her propeller regularly.

While the *Rattler* was being built, Brunel was anxious to finish her and conduct trials, but the Navy wanted to build the ship properly. Brunel's anxiety was not unconnected with the imminent completion of the *Great Britain* – *Rattler* would provide important experimental data for the design of propellers and the gearing ratio. Launched at Sheerness on 12 April 1843, *Rattler* was the world's first screw propeller warship. Her machinery was installed in the East India Docks.

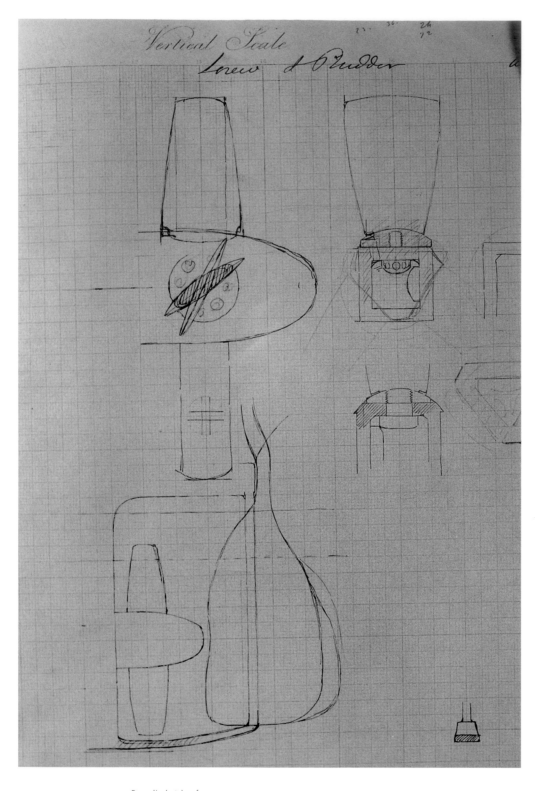

Vertical Scale
Screw & Rudder

Brunel's sketches for a
propeller and rudder –
possibly for the *Great
Eastern. University of
Bristol Library*

After th3 *Great Britain* was floated
from her building dock at Bristol on
19 July, Brunel was anxious to begin the
trials, which, at his insistence, would
be recorded with new thrust meters
and engine indicators. Brunel sought
consistent data, which would inform
the design process.

Brunel used the *Rattler* to explore the
best forms for screws and the ships that
were to use them, whether they were
sailing warships with low-powered
auxiliary steam plants or full powered
Atlantic liners. *Rattler* first raised steam
on 24 October 1843, and over the next
nine months Brunel directed a series of
trials that developed the world's first
efficient propeller.

Although the Admiralty was only
interested in a low-speed auxiliary system
capable of 6 knots, Brunel designed screw
forms for twice that speed. During this
time the length of the screw was reduced
from 5ft 9in to 1ft 3in, and the diameter
increased as far as practical. Brunel's work
advanced the theoretical and practical
understanding of screw propulsion to
the point where it could be adopted by
the Royal Navy for all future warships
without risk of failure.

After *Rattler's* first trial on Monday
30 October 1843, when she made 8 knots,
Brunel directed Maudslay's to reduce the
length of the screw in accordance with
Smith's directions. The following day
Brunel instructed Field to alter the screw,
and advised Smith how this should
be done.

For the next trial he wanted the ship
deeper in the water and requested a

BRUNEL AND THE SCREW PROPELLER

shelter on the upper deck from which to record his results.

A journey to Ireland on railway business gave him time to reflect on the reasons for the relatively low speeds achieved on the early trials. On his return, he advised Smith to measure the pitch of both blades of the propeller 'very accurately' as he suspected they might differ from each other. He also asked Field how long it would take to make another screw, and enquired how far the small drum on the drive shaft could be enlarged, as this would increase the gear ratio between engine and propeller revolutions.

Although the initial trials had already halved the length of the screw to only three feet, Brunel advised the Admiralty to establish the best performance of the two-blade screw before trying a three-blade screw of the same pitch and form. While this was sound practice, he remained anxious to prepare a four-blade screw.

The reason for his concern was the *Great Britain*, which was now in the process of being fitted out. He needed data from high-speed trials with *Rattler* in order to design the screw for *Great Britain*, but doubted whether *Rattler* would achieve the desired speed for another two months. So anxious was he to try *Rattler* with a multi-bladed screw that he suggested the *Great Western* Company itself should cast a four-bladed propeller for her.

At the end of the year, when Brunel went to Italy for three weeks, he advised Parry that it was essential to proceed carefully and thoroughly as:

… a great deal may be done with the screw but … we are quite in the dark about it – and in these experiments … I should hope that by proceeding very carefully and systematically we may enlighten ourselves.

Writing to Smith a month later he was more optimistic:

I find on my return a decidedly increased opinion, or conviction, on all hands that the days of paddle are numbered and that the age of screw is commenced.

After the fifth trial, on Saturday 2 February – when *Rattler* achieved 9.2 knots with a sharpened two-blade screw – Brunel was ready to try three blades. This trial convinced him that the *Great Britain's* screw should be bent at the tip, rather than all along the blade. He altered the pitch of the blades after the sixth trial with the three-bladed screw, and recognised the need for greater diameter. The sixth trial demonstrated that the three-blade screw was too long.

Recognising the limitations of Smith's preliminary work (and his weakness as a theoretical and experimental engineer) Brunel knew that the future of the screw as an efficient propeller rested in his hands. He advised Smith that the new four-bladed screw need only be 18 inches long, a figure that also applied to the new two-bladed screw. He also offered him the concept of a variable pitch on the blades of the screw (which he was already using in his design for the *Great Britain's* screw) so that Smith could patent it, 'and strengthen your original patent as it is more fully applicable to your screw than any of the forms claimed by others.'

Evidently he had not read Smith's patent, which did not concern the screw, only the location. Smith, for his part, was too polite to point this out.

The seventh and eighth trials used the three-blade screw, now shortened twice. By 5 March 1844 the *Rattler* had proved itself capable of travelling at 9.2 knots with a modified two-blade screw. It should be stressed that this was more than 50% faster than the Admiralty had intended, and provided far more useful information for Brunel and the *Great Britain* than it did for the Admiralty. The success of this trial was particularly timely, for the Directors of the Great Western Steamship Company now instructed Brunel to proceed with the design of the propeller for the *Great Britain*. Clearly, they had been waiting for further data from the *Rattler* trials – probably on Brunel's advice.

Detail from Scott Russell's longitudinal plan of the *Great Eastern, c.*1860, showing the screw propeller machinery. *Science Museum*

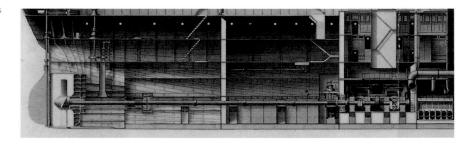

Brunel's six-bladed screw for the *Great Britain* has been demonstrated to be 'extraordinarily efficient', comparing well with modern designs. This was hardly surprising: it was based on data generated by *Rattler* at the Admiralty's expense. This propeller was built up from a central boss, with the blades welded on and extension plates riveted onto the tips of the blades. Brunel also designed a more robust four-bladed cast bronze screw, which was fitted after the six-bladed version broke up on *Great Britain's* second voyage.

Even more significant was Brunel's response to the problem of designing a screw propeller ship. The *Great Britain* used a strikingly modern balanced rudder, 'brilliantly designed to suit screw propulsion and much ahead of its time'. It was the ability to conceive of the ship as an integrated whole, using design to ensure that it was more than the sum of its parts, which made Brunel the leading figure in the development of efficient screw propulsion. When the *Great Britain* entered service she performed almost exactly as Brunel had predicted – making her speed at the intended engine revolutions. With any other designer in such a new field this would have been remarkable: with Brunel it was only to be expected.

During the *Rattler* trials Brunel constantly refined the screw design, reducing the length, and making the blades sharper to pass through water more easily. The eleventh trial on 11 March, reinforced his conclusion that increased diameter was needed. So Brunel advised the Navy to order a two-blade

screw of 10 foot diameter, with the pitch at the centre considerably less than at the outside, like the *Great Britain* screw. With this screw he expected her to make 10 knots, but the Navy had no interest in further experimental work.

Brunel, however, persuaded them to continue. Convinced that there was no need for any increase in pitch, Brunel urged Smith and Maudslay's to improve the Smith screw according to his own ideas, with a new two-blade screw of 10-foot diameter. His interpretation was largely confirmed by the seventeenth trial on 23 April, when a new Smith two-blade screw created only 16% slip in reaching 9.8 knots. This was the last trial that Brunel attended, but he pressed for further experimental work – still at the Navy's expense, it should be noted.

With the fundamental experimental phase effectively over, *Rattler* became a regular warship. It was time to create an integrated screw steamship design, which, as Brunel had stressed years before, would minimise the impact of the screw on the ship. As if to prove the point *Rattler* finally made 10 knots on 27 June, using the new screw.

The *Rattler* trials had gone far beyond the original intention of the Navy, and the most significant results were quickly forgotten. Even so, by hiring Brunel, the Navy had saved itself time and money. Brunel's own object in joining the project had been to advance research and experimental work for the *Great Britain*. So, while *Great Britain's* trials in January 1845 were a triumph for Brunel, they owed much to the *Rattler*.

Although Brunel did not invent the screw propeller he, more than anyone else, ensured its adoption. He was responsible for the success of HMS *Rattler*, the world's first screw propeller warship, by designing her engineering plant and running the trials programme.

These trials resulted in the creation of the first efficient propeller. And Brunel was the first to use the information they generated, designing six and four bladed fixed propellers for the *Great Britain* – the world's first full powered oceanic screw steamship. Whilst he himself had benefited from the use of naval vessels for full-scale propeller experiments, Brunel provided the Navy with priceless input into the development of efficient propellers.

His design philosophy was clearly set out in 1843:

We must adopt a principle not to be departed from, that all mechanical difficulties of construction must give way, must in fact be lost sight of in determining the most perfect form. If we find that the screw determined upon cannot be made (and what cannot be done?) then it is quite time to try another form and even then my rule would be to try again at making it.

When he came to design the *Great Eastern* nearly a decade later, Brunel adopted a unique screw and paddle wheel system – but the latter was only to enable his ship to operate in confined spaces.

His attention to detail, and insistence on accurate trials and careful recording of data, remain as the basis of development engineering. This reflected the breadth of vision and design skill that made him the leading professional engineer of the age and inspired the establishment of his profession.

Drawing of the propeller of the *Great Britain*.
SS Great Britain Trust

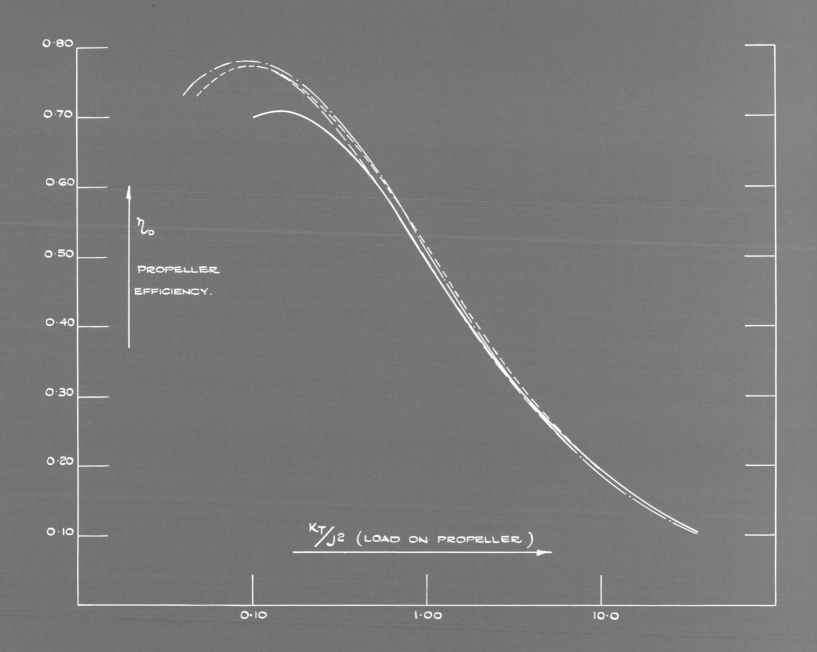

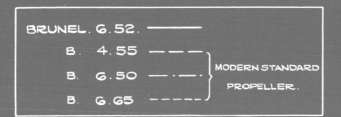

A model of the SS *Great Britain* was used by David Moor at Vicker's Experimental Tank at St Albans to test the efficiency of her propulsion compared to modern propellers. The results are plotted on the graph below, with the solid line representing Brunel's propeller and dotted lines representing modern four- and six-bladed propellers.

At the design point it was at peak efficiency and only about 5% less efficient than a modern six-bladed propeller. At heavy loadings it was equally efficient.

Dr E. Corlett, author of *The Iron Ship* and David Moor.

BRUNEL. 6.52. ⸺

B. 4.55 ⸺ ⸺

B. 6.50 ⸺ · ⸺ · } MODERN STANDARD PROPELLER.

B. 6.65 ⸺ ⸺

η_o

PROPELLER EFFICIENCY.

K_T/J^2 (LOAD ON PROPELLER.)

0·80
0·70
0·60
0·50
0·40
0·30
0·20
0·10

0·10   1·00   10·0

8 THE LEVIATHAN
DESIGNING THE *GREAT EASTERN*

Denis Griffiths

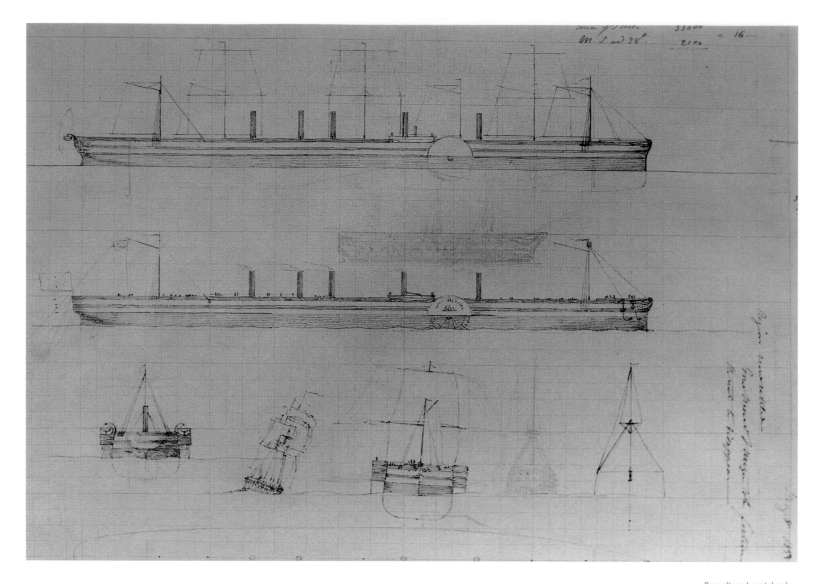

Brunel's early notebook
sketches for the *Great
Eastern*, 1853.
*University of Bristol
Library*

Previous page
Bow of the *Great
Eastern*, with the
launching ways visible,
photographed by
Robert Howlett,
2 November 1857.
*National Maritime
Museum B1699C*

B RUNEL WAS A DESIGNER OF engineering works – essentially a consultant who provided an engineering service to his clients for a fee. Yet such was his passion for ship building that he gave his services free to the Great Western Steamship Company, the owners of the *Great Western* and *Great Britain*.

These two Brunel-designed ships, the precursors to the *Great Eastern,* were revolutionary and record-breaking. The *Great Western* was the first steamer built specifically to ply the North Atlantic, and missed by only a few hours the distinction of being the first ship to travel from the British Isles to New York under steam. The *Great Britain* was the first large ocean-going ship to be built of iron, and the first to cross the Atlantic using screw propulsion. When she was launched in 1843, the *Great Britain* was the largest ship in the world at 322ft.

But even she was dwarfed by Brunel's final ship, the *Great Eastern* – an incredible 692ft long, with a gross tonnage of 18,915 tons and accommodation for 4,000 passengers. Nothing as long would be built for the next forty-one years; nothing would exceed her in tonnage until the *Lusitania* was launched forty-eight years later. Yet the *Great Eastern* is generally considered to be Brunel's most notorious failure. In commercial operation it undoubtedly was, but from an engineering viewpoint the situation is not so clear-cut.

Engineers have a duty to provide their employers with goods or services of the quality required and within the budget agreed. Undeniably, the building costs of

the *Great Eastern* far exceeded the original estimate, but that was not entirely Brunel's fault, as the directors of the Eastern Steam Navigation Company (for whom the ship was built) accepted a ridiculously low tender from the shipbuilder John Scott Russell. Subsequent changes in ownership of the vessel before she entered service, resulted in her not being operated on the route originally intended. As a consequence, the *Great Eastern* had to ply her maritime trade wherever opportunity knocked, and she effectively became a tramp steamer rather than a luxurious passenger and cargo liner. This was not the purpose for which Brunel had designed her.

There are two guiding considerations in the design of any ship: the operational design, which dictates factors such as size and shape; and the engineering design, concerning naval architecture and marine engineering. Brunel's concept for the *Great Eastern* was bold in both.

Using his experience with *Great Western* and *Great Britain*, he determined her size and layout for the operating route; he planned her hull structure to ensure that she would be strong enough to contend with any maritime hazard she would meet, and he decided what system of propulsion she would have.

What he did not do was dictate how the hull would be formed, nor specify what type of engines would be used or how they should be arranged – he only specified the power requirement. Brunel's job was rather to ensure that the ship was built to his general requirements – or to any specific plans he might produce – and

to oversee all aspects of construction to ensure that they met with his approval.

In 1851, the Australian Mail Company had requested Brunel's advice on the best size and class of ship to operate a mail service from Britain to Australia. He recommended the building of iron ships of 5,000 or 6,000 tons capacity, as that size of ship would only require one stop for coal at the Cape of Good Hope. The availability of coal was the major problem with oceanic steamship operation. The conventional view was that there were only two solutions to this – send supplies from Britain or obtain coal locally. However, Brunel had encountered problems with the *Great Western* when local coal obtained at New York was of indifferent quality and caused steaming problems, whilst coal sent from Britain and stockpiled at New York was charged import duty.

He knew that there would be additional difficulties involved with a voyage to Australia or India because of the greater distance. Ships taking coal from Britain to these overseas stations could be delayed or lost thus harming operating schedules. This factor must have influenced his views on the size of ship needed for the service and would certainly have been one of the reasons for advising on 6,000 ton ships.

The idea was bold – as were all Brunel's schemes – too bold for some directors of the company, and at their insistence the plans were scaled down. Despite this, Brunel agreed to become their Consulting Engineer. Two smaller iron steam ships, *Victoria* and *Adelaide*, were ordered and built by John Scott Russell, with the general design work being done by Brunel.

However, Brunel was now thinking beyond a ship which needed to make a break in its journey, and decided that the solution was for a ship to carry its own bunkers for a complete round trip to Australia or India. It would have to be very large indeed, but scale did not worry Brunel – it was just another engineering challenge that could be resolved by the application of sound reasoning and plenty of money.

As with all of his other projects he prepared well and collected much data relating to trade between Britain and Eastern countries. Using this information he formulated his proposal for the construction of large steamers to operate a service between Britain and the East.

In February and March 1852 I matured my ideas of the large ship with nearly all my present details, and in March I made my first sketch of one with paddles and screw. The size I then proposed was 600 feet by 70 feet, and in June and July I determined on the mode of construction now adopted of cellular bottom; intending to make the outer skin of wood for the sake of coppering.

Making the outer skin of wood, with copper sheathing to prevent attack by wood-boring worms, was a novel concept for an iron ship but was probably considered essential because of the ineffective anti-fouling coatings then available for iron hulls, whereas the success of copper sheathing for wooden hulls had been established in the mid-eighteenth century.

Having formulated his ideas, Brunel discussed the concept with a number of people including Scott Russell and

Christopher Claxton, and later, in July 1852, with directors from the Eastern Steam Navigation Company (which had been formed in 1851 with the specific intention of securing mail contracts from Britain to the East Indies and Australia). By the end of the year the company gave Brunel permission to undertake more detailed design work and to seek tenders for the construction of a ship and its machinery.

Yet the Eastern Steam Navigation Company had already failed to secure any contract, and the nature of its tender submission is further indication of the directors' loose thinking on shipping matters. Their vague and rather amateurish approach effectively gave Brunel a free hand to design and build the *Great Eastern*. In the language of modern business, the company had not conducted a proper feasibility study. No detailed investigation into the trade between Britain and the East had been carried out, nor had the directors considered the effect of suddenly landing a vast cargo of goods would have on the prices which could then be fetched for those goods. However, the Company did have Brunel on their side. But he believed that others involved in the project had the same devotion to it as himself – unfortunately, this was not to prove the case.

Brunel's sketchbooks show a number of ideas for the arrangement of the ship, and it is clear that the size and propulsion system were the result of careful consideration. Whilst still deciding upon the dimensions for the ship, Brunel had commissioned a series of hull friction

experiments to test the relative frictional values of copper and painted iron, as, at that time, he still intended that the outer part of the double hull would be copper-sheathed wood.

The proposed ship would require more powerful machinery than had ever been installed in a ship and there were engineering limitations. A single screw propulsion system would require a massive propeller shaft, much larger than anything ever built, and the thrust block would certainly present difficulties; the actual making of the screw would be an engineering feat in itself. The alternative, twin screws, were a possibility but

John Scott Russell by Henry Wyndham Phillips. *Scottish National Portrait Gallery*

The *Great Eastern* in the final stages of her launch, January 1858. *The Illustrated Times*

shipbuilders had very little experience of such systems. Brunel was certainly not averse to novelty but the fitting of twin propellers in his gigantic ship must have seemed to be pushing the bounds of experimentation just a little too far.

Paddle wheels were less efficient than screw propellers but they did have advantages, particularly in shallow draft conditions. If the ship was going to reach Calcutta, the shallow waters of India's River Hoogly would have to be navigated, and the depth of water there, and at other possible ports, limited the maximum draught of the ship. Brunel had done his own research and knew that the maximum draught to allow the ship to navigate the Hoogly was 24ft. This figure became critical. It governed the ship's other dimensions for an anticipated tonnage and that allowed him to perform basic calculations concerning the necessary power to drive the ship at the intended speed of 15 knots.

The draught was also critical with regard to the operation of the propeller, which needed to be fully immersed in order to get maximum propulsive power. This new ship would be larger than any yet built and it was essential that it had full power available for manoeuvring. But a single propeller would have too large a diameter to be fully immersed at a draught of 24ft. The single propeller by itself, therefore, would not be sufficient. The only solution was to adopt a combined screw and paddle wheel drive.

The use of both paddles and screw resulted in two engine rooms and boiler rooms which had to be located close by the machinery in order to reduce steam losses. The power of the engines dictated how much steam would be required. A steam pressure of 24psi was typical for the period, and that, in turn, dictated how large the boiler plant would be. Although contractors would supply boilers and engines, Brunel was able to estimate the space these would take in the hull and hence, to some extent, the machinery layout designed itself.

In order to make the ship profitable on a return voyage from India, Brunel argued that a displacement of 21,000 tons was required but, as has already been said, he only had a maximum draught of 24ft upon leaving the Hoogly. From this he was able to compute possible lengths and breadths for the ship but there were many combinations from which to choose. Brunel had studied ship forms and was keen to ensure a smooth flow of water around the hull and to reduce the problem of rolling. He finally decided upon a length of 670ft and a breadth of 85ft, with a deep-water draught of 30ft when fully loaded. That allowed for a draught of 23ft when making the return passage from the Hoogly because more than half of the coal would have been burned by then. Curiously, he does not seem to have considered the possibility of taking water ballast on board to maintain a deep draught for the return journey.

In the summer of 1852, it seems that a fleet of large ships was contemplated and the initial idea was to construct two at the same time. Brunel advised the directors that they must '… be exact duplicates of each other.' He was to be responsible for the ship design, preparing the contracts and detailing the ship's specifications – thus his powers were considerable.

The contract for constructing the hull was given to John Scott Russell, whose shipyard was at Millwall on the Thames, and he agreed to very strict terms, financially and in many other respects.

The contract, signed in December 1853:

… provided for the construction, launch, trial and delivery of an iron ship of the general dimensions 680 feet between perpendiculars, 83 feet beam and 58 feet deep according to the drawings annexed signed by the Engineer, I. K. Brunel. … No cast iron

to be used anywhere except for slide valves and cocks without special permission of the Engineer. ... The ship to be built in a dock. ... All calculations, drawings, models and templates which the contractor may prepare shall from time to time be submitted to the Engineer for his revision, alteration or approval. The Engineer to have entire control over the proceedings and the workmanship.

Scott Russell's price for the hull was £275,200 – exceptionally low, as Brunel would have realised considering the cost of constructing the *Great Britain*. It is difficult to understand why he did not comment. Possibly Brunel believed that if the project did not get started at that time it never would and, as with many other schemes, additional funding would eventually be found to complete the work. Scott Russell even offered to reduce the price to £258,000 if he was awarded the contract for the second ship. The directors, seemingly prudent for once, decided to construct only one ship initially.

Brunel had his own ideas on iron ship construction. From his experience with the *Great Britain*, Brunel developed his idea of longitudinal framing and then combined this and transverse strengthening in his cellular concept. Longitudinal framing was not new – Scott Russell had first used it in 1834 on the 70ft *Storm*.

The *Great Britain* had been built using a clinker system for arranging the plates, but this resulted in gaps between the overlapping plate and the frame and tapered strips of iron had be used to fill the gaps. Scott Russell had the idea of arranging plates in a manner (sometimes referred to as 'in and out') where alternate plates were riveted directly to the frames

and the plates connected to these were raised above the frame – the gaps between these plates and the frames being filled with parallel strips of iron. Brunel approved of the 'in and out' system of plating but was not happy with the use of the filler strips. In a memorandum written in February 1854 after checking some of Scott Russell's detailed drawings he wrote:

It is evident that large weights may most easily be wasted or saved by a careless or close consideration of the best application of iron in every single detail. I found, for instance, an unnecessary introduction of a filling piece or strip, such as is frequently used in ship-building to avoid bending to angle irons; made a slight alteration in the disposition of the plates that rendered this unnecessary; found that we thus saved 40 tons weight of iron, or say £1,200 of money in first cost, and 40 tons of cargo freight – at least £3,000 a year.

This was characteristic of Brunel's capacity – he could mastermind a ship larger and more powerful than any that had been built, yet at the same time he had a grasp of detail which could identify issues like this.

In the same memorandum he went on to state:

The principle of construction of the ship is in fact entirely new, if merely from the rule which I have laid down, and shall rigidly preserve, that no materials shall be employed at any part except at the place, and in the direction, and in the proportion, in which it is required, and can be usefully employed for the strength of the ship, and none merely for the purpose of facilitating the framing and first construction.

Every piece of iron which went into the ship had to serve the purpose of adding to the strength and that included the framing. Frames were not used simply as places to which the side plating was attached, they were actual strength members of the hull structure.

In the present construction of iron ships ... nearly 20 per cent of the total weight is expended in angle irons or frames which may be useful or convenient in the mere putting together of the whole as a great box, but is almost useless, or very much misapplied, in affecting the strength of the structure of the ship. All this misconstruction I forbid, and the consequence is that every part has to be considered and designed as if an iron ship had never before been built; indeed I believe we should get on much quicker if we had no previous habits and prejudices on the subject.

The *Great Eastern's* bulkheads. *D. Griffiths*

This shows Brunel at his best: he had returned to first principles, looking at the ship as a floating iron structure rather than an iron development of a traditional wooden hull. By this time the idea of using a double skin with an outer layer of coppered wood had clearly been abandoned, and the hull of the ship was to be constructed entirely from iron.

Within the statement is an implied rebuke to Scott Russell for employing the earlier ideas he had used for smaller ships. Rivalry between the two men as to whom should be considered the father of the ship simmered and often boiled over throughout the years of construction. Brunel considered himself as both the originator of the project and designer of the ship and took offence when he felt that he was not being given due credit. In November 1854 a long article about the ship appeared in one of the London newspapers and it mentioned Brunel only once, 'Mr Brunel, the Engineer of the Eastern Steam Navigation Company, approved of the project, and Mr Scott Russell undertook to carry out the design'. Brunel wrote to the secretary of the company:

I cannot allow it to be stated, apparently on authority, while I have the whole heavy responsibility of its success resting on my shoulders, that I am a mere passive approver of the project of another, which in fact originated solely with me, and has been worked out by me at great cost of labour and thought devoted to it now for not less than three years.

A little later, Brunel received a letter from Scott Russell in which he stated that he had told Prince Albert that Brunel was the 'Father' of the ship. The letter was obsequious to a fault and Scott Russell appears to have been trying to curry favour with Brunel. In a letter to *The Times,* in April 1857, Scott Russell appeared to be glowing in his praise, and confirmed his earlier expressed opinion that Brunel originated the concept of the ship and was responsible for the design. At this time the Eastern Steam Navigation Company was in serious financial trouble and Scott Russell may well have been trying to distance himself from responsibility for any failure:

My share of the merit and responsibility is that of builder of the ship for the Eastern Steam Navigation Company. I designed her lines and constructed the iron hull of the ship and am responsible for her merits or defects as a piece of naval architecture.

He was clearly accepting no blame for the financial situation, although he had grossly underestimated the construction cost, nor did he want people to believe

The *Great Eastern* under construction, 18 August 1855. *National Maritime Museum D0676D.*

Overleaf
The *Great Eastern* and the forward checking drum, photographed by Robert Howlett, 2 November 1857. *National Maritime Museum B1699A*

Building the steamship Great Eastern by William Parrott. *National Maritime Museum BHC3384*

that he had anything to do with the launching due later that year. In explaining Brunel's part in the project Scott Russell did give an insight into the principle upon which construction was based.

It is to the company's engineer, Mr I. K. Brunel, that the original conception is due ... It was his idea also to introduce a cellular construction like that at the top and bottom of the Britannia Bridge [designed by Robert Stephenson and opened in 1850] into the construction of the great ship.

Unwilling to give too much praise he then claimed to be the originator of the construction methods used:

Her lines and her structure in other respects are identical with those of my other ships, which are constructed like this on a principle of my own, which I have systematically carried out during the last twenty years, and which is commonly called the "wave"[1] principle. In other respects also, her materials are put together in the manner usual in my other ships.

Brunel evolved the idea of a cellular structure at the bottom and top of the hull in order to form a rigid box arrangement, Britannia Bridge-style, as he worked through the problems of the strength of the ship.

His notebooks are littered with drawings and calculations reflecting the most severe conditions the ship was likely to encounter. For instance, treating the ship as a beam, he investigated the loading if the vessel grounded on two points 400ft apart – a highly unlikely condition.

From his calculations he formed the conclusion that if this occurred the bottom of the ship would need to be made from iron plate 90ft wide and four or five inches thick, to keep the stress within acceptable limits. Clearly this would not have been practical and such calculations would have led him to the use of a cellular structure rather than mass to give strength. Although Brunel did not originate this concept, he did apply it creatively to iron ships.

It was obvious to Brunel that such a large ship could not be dry-docked because there were no suitable facilities in existence, or even planned, and so she would have to be grounded on a gridiron in order to enable routine hull maintenance to be undertaken. He informed the directors of the action he had taken to allow for this: 'We have flattened the floor and strengthened it considerably so as to allow of the vessel being safely grounded on a gridiron or even if partially waterborne, on a beach.'

This grounding requirement, and possibly the implications of operating the ship far away from good repair facilities, may have led him to consider the idea of the watertight double bottom. The cellular structure did not have to be watertight, and making it so did present additional constructional problems – but Brunel certainly saw the advantages, and the watertight double bottom extended from the bottom of the ship to the normal loaded waterline.

From his experiences with the *Great Britain*, which was grounded at Dundrum Bay in Ireland for almost a year, he was aware of the consequences of shell plating being punctured. Inner and outer double bottom plating was 1in thick and the plates were spaced 2ft 10in apart, the longitudinal frames in the double bottom being placed 6ft apart. The upper cellular structure was constructed in a similar manner. Not content with the strengthening provided by the two cellular structures, Brunel fitted two longitudinal bulkheads, 350ft long and 36ft deep, to impart additional longitudinal strength. These were located in the middle part of the ship and placed each side of the engine and boiler rooms.

As a ship rolls there is a tendency for its hull to distort and move from a rectangular shape to that of a parallelogram. Brunel was well aware of this problem and knew that the solution lay in having enough transverse bulkheads to give the necessary rigidity to the structure. He modified Scott Russell's drawings to give what he considered the correct number of transverse bulkheads and, as he reported to the directors in February 1855:

The whole of the vessel is divided transversely into ten separate perfectly water-tight compartments by bulkheads carried up to the upper deck, and

consequently far above the deepest water lines, even if the ship were water-logged, so far as such a ship could be; and these are not nominal divisions, but complete substantial bulkheads, water-tight and of strength sufficient to bear the pressure of the water, should a compartment be ever filled with water; so that if the ship were supposed to be cut in two, the separate portions would float. Besides these principal bulkheads there is in each compartment a second intermediate bulkhead, forming a coal bunker, and carried up to the main-deck, which can, in an emergency, also be closed. There are no openings under the deep-water line through the principal bulkheads, except one continuous gallery or tunnel near the water line through which the steam pipes pass, and which will be so constructed as to remain closed, the opening being the exception, and the closing again being easy, and the height being such that, under the most improbable circumstances of damage to the ship, ample time would be afforded to close it leisurely, and to make it perfectly water-tight. The transverse bulkheads being perfect, there being only one door – and that of iron –

in each, at one of the upper decks, all currents of air or means of communicating fire may be completely cut off; and with... the most ample means of supplying water, I believe that all possibility of danger from fire may be completely prevented.

Throughout the period he was considering the power plant for the ship, Brunel was in constant communication with his friend Joshua Field, who considered that the steam pressure should not exceed 15psi on the grounds that mechanical problems increased with pressure, but the gains did not increase at the same rate. Brunel agreed but retained an open mind as to what the final steam pressure should be. Field was very much against the steam jacketing of cylinders

Brunel watching the failed launch of the Great Eastern, November 1857, photographed by Robert Howlett. On Brunel's right is William Jacomb, his Resident Engineer for the project. *National Portrait Gallery*

but Brunel favoured this practice. By 17 July 1852, Brunel had decided that the screw engines should deliver 60 per cent of the required power and the paddle engines 40 per cent. In a memorandum dated 28 April 1853 he wrote:

We are now seeking tenders for the engines and ship ... screw engine, indicated horse-power 4,000; nominal horse-power 1,600; paddle, indicated horse-power 2,600; nominal horse-power 1,000; to work with steam 15lb to 25lb; speed of screw 45 to 55 revolutions; paddle 10 to 12.

Three proposals were submitted for the machinery:

Mr Blake, of the firm Watt & Co., and Mr J. S. Russell and Mr Humphrys, have as I had before reported, devoted much attention to the subject: from these gentlemen I have received distinct well-considered designs of the screw and paddle-engines. I have been in frequent communication with these gentlemen, and have seen their plans while in progress, and have made my suggestions upon them, and assisted more or less in maturing them, and at all events in preventing the adoption of any principle or arrangement that I should afterwards object to.

Brunel considered the screw engine to be the most important part of the *Great Eastern's* propulsion system:

The principal part of the propelling power of the ship will be thrown upon the screw; and upon these engines therefore will mainly depend the performance of the ship, and particularly upon their constant never-failing working, probably for thirty or forty days and nights, must depend the certainty of the ship's performance ... The extreme simplicity of Mr Blake's engine leads me to prefer it. As regards the paddle engine, I unhesitatingly give preference to that proposed by Mr Scott Russell.

The paddle machinery was, it would appear, ancillary and he left much of the design work to Scott Russell. However, that he checked drawings and inspected parts at various stages of manufacture is evident from a memorandum of 10 March 1854: 'Engaged all afternoon at Millwall ... settled and signed drawings of crank and piston rods'. Again, this indicates more than just a passive role in the venture but one of active involvement as he had to approve of all engineering which went into the ship.

Brunel was aware of the need for adequate governing of engine speed – even before he learned of the incident aboard HMS *Agamemnon* on 9 November

1853, when serious damage resulted from over-speeding of the engine after she lost her screw. 'August 7 – Memorandum for engines – Very sensitive governors to be applied to both engines to prevent running away'. After the *Agamemnon* incident he wrote

There is no reason why a sensitive governor should not act in less than one revolution of the crank, and act upon a tumbler which should shut off instantly the expansion valve (query, hydraulic governors).

Neither Scott Russell nor Joshua Field were happy about using feed water heaters located around the base of the funnels (an idea taken from the *Great Britain*) but Brunel insisted that they were fitted to the two forward funnels, from the paddle engine boilers. Each heater jacket, constructed from half inch iron plate, extended from the top of the boiler uptake to the main deck and formed a six inch annulus around the funnel uptake. Feed water was pumped into the heater and flowed upwards to an outlet near the top of the heater from whence it passed to the

The stern of the *Great Eastern*, photographed by Robert Howlett, 3 November 1857. *National Maritime Museum B1699B*

The *Great Eastern's* propeller boss. *National Maritime Museum A4943*

CRE
LON

boiler; unlike that fitted in the *Great Britain* these heaters employed force feed of water to the boilers and not gravity feed.

A vent pipe was fitted at the top of the heater annulus and this extended upwards about 30ft before venting into the stokehold. The vent pipe was fitted with a stopcock which could be closed in order to allow the heater annulus to be pressure tested, but which should have been open in normal service. Unfortunately, during the first passage from London the cock on the forward funnel heater was closed, allowing pressure to build up as water turned to steam. Eventually an explosion occurred resulting in furnace blowback and the fatal injury of five stokers. However, this was the result of human error, not Brunel's engineering.

Brunel's principal failure was the launch of the ship. No small episode in the history of this ingenious engineer and his remarkable ship – but a major event in itself.

It had been stated in the tender documents that the ship was to be built in a dock. However, it had quickly become obvious that the construction of a dock would be prohibitively expensive. Therefore it had to be built above high water level. The angle of the slipway for a lengthwise launch would have resulted in the highest part of the hull being some 100ft above ground level, causing major difficulties with the primitive lifting gear which then existed. The hull would also have been subjected to high strains during launch when the stern was afloat but the bow was still supported by its cradle on the slipway.

A sideways launch was the only solution. The area in which the ship was to be built and launched had to be strengthened by some 1,500 timber piles, 24ft long being driven into the ground and bound together by longitudinal and transverse timbers, before a thick bed of concrete was poured between them. Brunel had iron rails laid on the launching ways, which were constructed in the same manner.

Furthermore, Brunel would not consider a free launch due to the inherent dangers this posed to the hull. It had to be a launch which he could control. The lower faces of the cradles were faced with iron strips which ran parallel to the axis of the ship. This he considered would reduce friction. The large cradles had a support area of some 19,200 square foot, which produced a bearing pressure of about

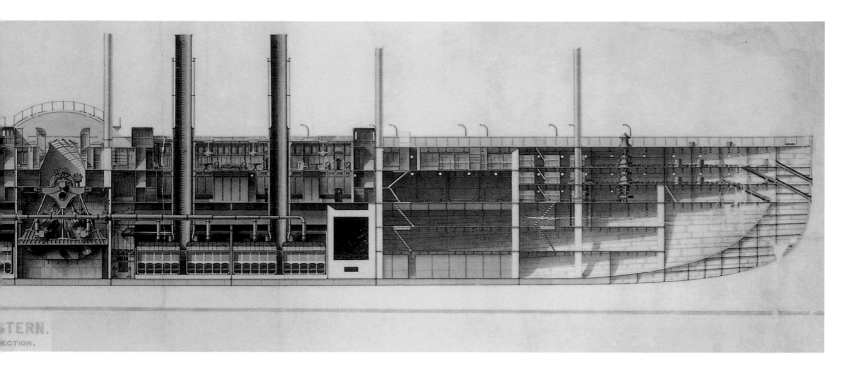

0.6 tons per square foot, much less than that accepted for free launches at that time. There should therefore have been no problem in keeping the ship moving, and Brunel believed that the real difficulty would be in regulating the speed of descent down the slipway.

In order to regulate this descent, two brakes were fitted, one to each cradle. Massive chains were attached to the cradles and these were wound around 9ft diameter drums, 120ft long, with the chain being paid out as required by the descent. Band brakes were fitted to each of the drums thus allowing control of the rate at which the chain was paid out. A system of chains, pulleys and windlasses was arranged so that an initial pull could be exerted on the hull in order to get it moving. Technically, the system was all that should have been required,

but nature – in the form of friction and gravity – decided otherwise.

During the launch the ship did move, though grudgingly, and it became obvious that things were not going according to plan. Brunel persisted – he had no alternative – and after many attempts, during which movement could be measured in inches rather than feet, he decided that the ship needed to be pushed down the incline

Brute force in the form of hydraulic rams was the solution, and the firm of Tangyes of Birmingham was enlisted to provide them. Richard Tangye was later to comment, 'We launched the *Great Eastern* and they launched us.' Even with the twenty-one hydraulic rams, progress was slow and it was not until the end of January 1858, some three months after the launch started,

that the great mass of the *Great Eastern* was afloat.

Brunel had certainly made mistakes in his assessment of the situation, and to make matters worse the launch was conducted in the full glare of the public – because the directors of the company had sold spectator tickets in order to recoup some of their expenditure.

The launch took far longer than it should have, but it can be considered a triumph of sorts, as Brunel – despite seriously failing health – never gave up on the challenge. His engineering solution, utilising hydraulic force, finally got his 'Great Ship' into the water.

Longitudinal section of the *Great Eastern*, c.1860, showing the machinery for both the screw propeller and paddle engines.
Science Museum

Overleaf:
The paddle engine room.
Illustrated London News

127

THE GREAT IRON SHIP – THE GREAT EASTERN

Fred Walker

Breathtaking Courage in Extrapolation

Brunel prepared the design of the *Great Eastern* on the basis of the minimum size that could sail around the world economically, with the fullest use of the technology of the time. He was working when the laws governing the engineering sciences were still being debated and formulated, and was therefore working beyond the limits of known technology. Kirkaldy's work on tensile strength had only just commenced in Robert Napier's shipyard, Rankine's work on thermodynamics was still to be published in Glasgow, and Froude (a former student trained of Brunel's) had not yet begun his brilliant study of hydronamics for the Admiralty.

Brunel's workbooks show his painstaking calculations with regard to the weight, carrying capacity, power and ultimately the fuel requirements for the prodigious ship.

His thinking was not constrained, and despite lack of statistical evidence on which to extrapolate, he designed the *Great Eastern* to be the largest ship in the world by a fair margin. Forty-one years were to pass before the *Oceanic* of 1899 surpassed her in length, and a remarkable forty-nine years before the Cunard liner, *Lusitania*, completed in 1907, exceeded her gross tonnage.

A Marketing Problem

Current ship designs are based on predicted market requirements from which the necessary size and carrying capacity is calculated. With this information the detailed design is generated and production organised.

Throughout her life the massive *Great Eastern* suffered from lack of demand. She had a relatively low passenger and cargo load, and her great size (especially her operating draft), limited the number of ports where fast turnaround and easy handling of passengers and cargo was achievable. Indeed, in the mid-nineteenth century, few ports could offer quays with water deep enough for this ship. Market requirements had been completely underestimated, and it was not until her days as a cable-layer that the massive holds and excellent carrying capacity could be turned to advantage.

Structural Strength

The girder strength of the *Great Eastern* shows that Brunel had a flair for structural design — a science then in its infancy. The ship had great reserves of strength, with longitudinal bulkheads giving massive girder strength and a steel deck offering the additional modular inertia of a 'top flange'. Unusual for the time were the transverse iron bulkheads, which gave both strength and watertight integrity.

The ship's double skin (or more correctly, the cellular double bottom) gave additional strength and security in the event of hull damage. It is interesting to note that 140 years later this feature is now becoming mandatory for large tankers in deep-sea operations.

Construction Material

At the time of the building of the *Great*

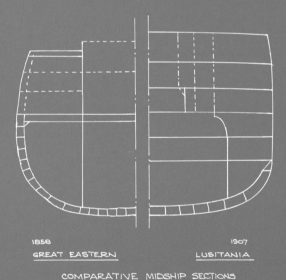

1858
GREAT EASTERN

1907
LUSITANIA

COMPARATIVE MIDSHIP SECTIONS

130

Eastern, iron had been in use as a ship building material for thirty years, but no contract anywhere in the world to that date had required over 6,000 tons (which was less than 23% of this ship's enormous displacement).

This compares favourably with the earlier *Great Britain*, where plate sizes varied depending on the rectangular mass of metal obtained from rolling a cast iron ingot. To ensure all such plates had suitable and adequate riveted landings, the frames had to be erected at differing distances apart to suit the most recent delivery of iron shell plates.

Stability
The design of the *Great Eastern* was such that she had a very large margin of stability.

However, there can be a cost when a ship has this characteristic, and that is heavy rolling in a seaway. Having a rounded mid-ship section, the *Great Eastern* had little resistance to movement around her fore and aft axis, and soon she had a bad reputation for having an unpleasant rolling motion.

In later years, the information gleaned from the rolling of the *Great Eastern,* was to aid William Froude in his now celebrated studies on the rolling of ships; and to reduce this hazard, changes were made to the shape of mid-ship sections, and bilge keels were often fitted.

Manoeuvrability
Ostensibly, the *Great Eastern* was a manoeuvrable ship and is comparable to modern ships in having two forms of propulsion — namely side paddles and a screw propeller. The paddles could drive her at over seven knots and with all systems in operation her top speed approached thirteen knots. She was not, however, easy to steer or manoeuvre, and after some experience in service her hand-operated steering gear had to be converted to steam operation. It seems strange that something as vital as the steering on such a large ship (where massive forces were involved) should be left to manual operation through a heavy chain and link gear.

Hull Form
Brunel showed perception in shaping the forward sections of the ship to reduce the effects of waves buffeting on flat and unresisting surfaces. He did not give the ship any sheer, which would have improved her looks. His reasoning may have been that, with the ship being so large, no reserve of buoyancy was needed for operation in heavy seas. The lack of sheer was a pity as it would have improved her appearance dramatically, although it would have made her construction more complicated.

Conclusion
The failure of *Great Eastern* came through her being designed for a market that had not been properly researched. She was just too large and built too soon for the technology of the time.

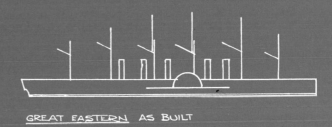

GREAT EASTERN AS BUILT

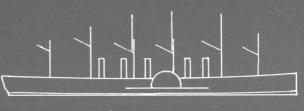

GREAT EASTERN
SHOWING ADVANTAGES OF SHEER

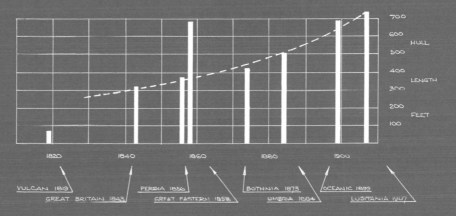

LENGTHS OF LEADING IRON & STEEL MERCHANT SHIPS
FROM 1819 TO 1907

F.M.W. SEP 2000

9 A CHRONOLOGY OF ISAMBARD KINGDOM BRUNEL

Adrian Vaughan

9 April 1806
Born in a terraced house in Britain Street, Portsea.

21 August 1822
Returns from Paris after schooling and apprenticeship under the great watchmaker, Louis Breguet. Joins his father's drawing office.

January 1823
His father, Marc Brunel, appointed Engineer of the Thames Tunnel.

April 1823
Marc gives Isambard the task of developing the 'Gaz' engine, designed to run on carbonic gas.

2 March 1825
Work begins on sinking the first shaft for the Thames Tunnel.

April 1826
Isambard appointed Acting Resident Engineer of the Thames Tunnel.

3 January 1827
Isambard promoted to the important rank of Resident Engineer of the Thames Tunnel.

18 May 1827
Tunnel roof collapses under the weight of the tide above.

20 May – 11 June 1827
Inspects river bed from diving bell. Supervising dumping of clay into hole created by tunnel collapse.

An undated portrait of Brunel.
Sotheby's London
(*Previous page,* detail)

Above right:
One of Brunel's early designs for the Clifton Bridge, dates 18 December 1830.
Science Museum

25 June 1827
Tunnel partially drained. Brunel uses a punt to inspect frames.

July 1827
Brunel escorts Charles Bonaparte (later Napoleon III) in a punt to view the frames.

7 October 1827
Brunel falls into ground level water tank at Tunnel works. Seriously hurt. Out of action until 24 October.

12 January 1828
6am Tunnel roof collapses. Brunel knocked unconscious and seriously injured.

4 February 1828
Feeling better, Brunel goes to Brighton to convalesce. Efforts with actresses bring on serious relapse.

June 1828
Brunel permitted to convalesce in Clifton, Bristol.

1829
Enters competition to design a bridge to cross the Avon Gorge. Submits four designs for four locations.

1829
Applies for post as Engineer of Newcastle & Carlisle Railway.

10 June 1830
Elected a Fellow of the Royal Society for his work on the Thames Tunnel, the Gaz engine, and his designs for Clifton Suspension Bridge.

October 1830
Installs a siphon to drain the sea marshes at Tollesbury, Essex.

16 March 1831
Brunel's design for a suspension bridge over the Avon Gorge at Clifton accepted.

20 May 1831
The astronomical observatory Brunel designed in London for James South is opened.

21 June 1831
Attends the ceremony to lay the foundation stone of Clifton Suspension Bridge.

30 October 1831
Civil insurrection and riots in Bristol. Brunel enlists as a Special Constable.

20 November 1831
Appointed Engineer of a new dock at Monkwearmouth, Sunderland. Resident Engineer: Michael Lane.

5 December 1831
Brunel takes his first ride on a railway, the Liverpool & Manchester. He writes: 'The time is not far off when we shall be able to take our coffee and write while going noiselessly and smoothly at 45 mph. Let me try.'

30 January 1833
After ten years unsuccessful work, Brunel finally abandons the Gaz engine.

February 1833
Designs dredging system for Bristol harbour. Appointed Engineer to supervise its construction and use.

21 February 1833
Submits his tender to make a survey of a railway from Bristol to London: the Bristol Railway.

7 March 1833
Appointed Surveyor of the Bristol Railway with Mr Townsend: Brunel writes: 'How the devil am I to get on with him tied round my neck?'

9 March 1833
Sets out on survey of Bristol Railway route.

30 July 1833
Publishes his plans for the Bristol Railway.

27 August 1833
Confirmed as Engineer of the Bristol Railway. Residents: George Frere, Bristol; John Hammond, London.

27 August 1833
Brunel first uses the title 'Great Western Railway' (GWR) for the Bristol Railway.

27 August 1833
Sets out on fully detailed survey of chosen route.

November 1833
Great Western Railway Bill goes before parliament. Terminus to be at Vauxhall Bridge.

25 July 1834
Bill thrown out by House of Lords.

31 August 1835
GWR Bill receives Royal Assent. Terminus to be at Euston.

15 September 1835
Proposes 7ft gauge for GWR.

September 1835
Engineer of Cheltenham & Great Western Union Railway (C&GWUR). Plans route Swindon – Gloucester – Cheltenham.

September 1835
Appointed Engineer of Bristol & Exeter Railway (B&ER). Resident: William Gravatt.

September 1835
Paddington Extension Railway surveyed.

September 1835
Working on designs for Maidenhead Bridge and Wharncliffe Viaduct. (The latter with considerable input from his father).

November 1835
Bill lodged for Paddington Extension Railway.

December 1835
Engineer of Merthyr & Cardiff Railway (M&CR) Taff Vale.

December 1835
Planning Reading – Newbury branch.

December 1835
Has agreed to act as Engineer of Hungerford Suspension Bridge over the Thames.

December 1835
Engineer of Bristol & Gloucester Railway (B&GR).

January 1836
Engineer of Great Western Steam Ship Company.

January 1836
Commences work on Box Tunnel.

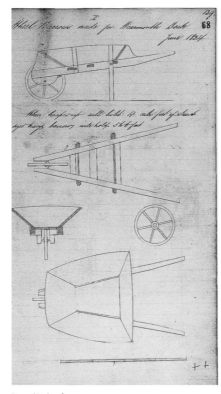

Brunel's plan for a wheelbarrow for Wearmouth Dock, 1834.
Public Record Office

June 1836
Surveys a Plymouth – Exeter railway. Line never built.

8 August 1836
Brunel writes impossible specifications to which his locomotives must be constructed.

22 July 1837
Launch of SS *Great Western* at Bristol

31 March 1838
SS *Great Western* steams from Millwall for Bristol. There is a fire in engine room and Brunel is seriously injured.

8 April 1838
SS *Great Western* leaves Avonmouth for New York.

4 June 1838
GWR opened to 22-mile post.

30 August 1838
Defends the broad gauge at shareholders' meeting. Brunel taken ill afterwards.

19 September 1838
He agrees to be bound by the directors. His broad gauge railway is criticised by John Hawkshaw.

November 1838 – June 1839
Brunel designs four versions of an iron hull for SS *Great Britain*.

11 December 1838
Replies to Hawkshaw's criticisms.

Swindon Locomotive Works in 2000.
Andrew Cross

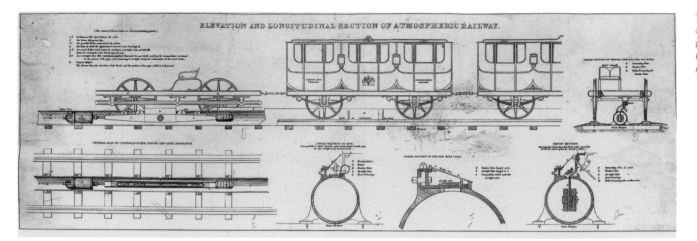

The principles of the atmospheric railway, possibly based on the Kingston & Dalkey line. *Public Record Office*

14 December 1838
Brunel offers to resign rather than accept a co-Engineer.

18 December 1838
Replies to Nicholas Wood's criticisms of the broad gauge.

29 December 1838
Brunel and Gooch's redesigned North Star locomotive produces a performance to silence all critics.

9 January 1839
Final trial of Brunel before directors and shareholders. North Star performance revealed. Meeting votes for Brunel and the broad gauge.

January 1839
Brunel-specified locomotives abandoned in favour of Daniel Gooch's designs.

19 July 1839
Keel laid for SS *Great Britain*: a 3,444 ton paddle steamer.

30 March 1840
GWR opens to Reading.

May 1840
Redesigns SS *Great Britain* hull for screw propeller. Starts to rebuild hull and design new engines.

1 June 1840
GWR opens to Steventon.

31 August 1840
GWR opens Bristol to Bath

17 December 1840
GWR opens Farringdon Road – Hay Lane.

31 May 1841
GWR opens Hay Lane – Chippenham.

31 May 1841
Cheltenham GW Union open Swindon – Cirencester.

May – July 1841
Brunel designs Swindon's station, locomotive works and workers' village.

14 June 1841
Bristol &Exeter Railway (B&ER) opens Bristol – Bridgwater and Weston branch

30 June 1841
GWR opens Chippenham – Bath. First through-train from Paddington to Bridgwater.

9 October 1841
Taff Vale Railway (TVR) opens Cardiff – Abercynon (15 miles).

1841
Appointed Engineer of the Oxford Railway (OR): Didcot – Oxford

1 July 1842
B&ER opens Bridgwater to Taunton.

1843
Visits Italy to engineer Genoa – Allessandria and Florence – Pistoia Railways. Appointed Engineer South Devon Railway (SDR).

3 April 1843
While performing a conjuring trick for his children, Brunel accidentally gets a sovereign stuck in his right lung.

17 April 1843
Sovereign commences to affect his breathing.

27 April 1843
Tracheotomy unsuccessfully performed on Brunel.

13 May 1843
4.30pm Brunel inverted on hinged table of his own design. Coin dislodged.

19 July 1843
Attends launch of SS *Great Britain* at Bristol for Great Western Steamship Company.

During 1844
Appointed Surveyor and Engineer of the following:
South Wales Railway (SWR): Gloucester – Swansea – Fishguard and branches (211 miles).

Wilts, Somerset & Weymouth Railway (WSWR): Thingley Junction (west of Chippenham) – Westbury – Salisbury – Frome – Yeovil – Dorchester – Weymouth and branches (148 miles).

Oxford, Worcester & Wolverhampton Railway (OWWR) (97 miles).

Berks & Hants Railway (B&HR): Reading – Basinstoke – Newbury – Hungerford (39 miles).

Oxford & Rugby Railway (O&RR): Oxford – Banbury – Fenny – Compton – Rugby (51 miles).

Monmouth & Hereford Railway (M&HR): Grange Court (on SWR) – Longhope – Ross-on-Wye – Hereford, Monmouth branch and others (45 miles).

Further visits to Italy as Engineer for Genoa – Allessandria Railway and Florence – Pistoia Railway.

1 May 1844
B&ER opened to Exeter.

12 June 1844
Oxford Railway opened from Didcot.

9 August 1844
Unreservedly recommends the atmospheric system of propulsion to the directors of the SDR.

12 December 1844
Brunel supervises SS *Great Britain's* departure to Millwall.

During 1845
Attends parliament as witness for numerous railway companies seeking to have their Acts approved.

1845
Proposes a high bridge over the River Tamar for the Cornwall Railway

January 1845
SS *Great Britain* steaming trials begin.

4 April 1845
Appears before Select Committee investigating atmospheric propulsion on railways.

1 May 1845
Hungerford footbridge opened.

12 May 1845
Cheltenham & Great Western Union Railway opened Kemble – Gloucester.

26 July 1845
Maiden voyage of SS Great Britain to New York.

26 August 1845
Appointed Engineer of the Cornwall Railway (CR): Plymouth – Falmouth (66 miles).

August 1845
Appointed Engineer of the West Cornwall Railway. (WCR) Truro – Penzance and branches (31 miles).

17 October 1845
Brunel appears before the Gauge Commissioners to defend his 7ft gauge.

February 1846.
Writes a detailed refutation of the Gauge Commissioners' Report, which is anti-broad gauge in its findings.

30 May 1846
South Devon Railway (SDR) opens Exeter Teignmouth. Locomotive hauled.

3 August 1846
Act obtained for Birmingham & Oxford Junction Railway. Brunel appointed Engineer.

23 September 1846
SS *Great Britain* runs aground in Dundrum Bay, Ireland.

December 1846
Brunel visits Dundrum Bay.

30 December 1846
SDR opens Teignmouth – Newton Abbott.

1847
Brunel designs 85ft x 6ft tubular coffer dam to survey Tamar riverbed for site of Royal Albert Bridge column.

20 July 1847
SDR opens Newton Abbott – Totnes. Steam hauled.

16 August 1847
SDR runs experimental atmospheric trains: Exeter –Teignmouth

August 1847
Brunel buys land at Watcombe, Torquay. Plans to build a chateau in an Anglo-Italian style country park.

27 August 1847
SS *Great Britain* salvaged. Great Western Steamship Company bankrupted as a result.

13 September 1847
Two public-service atmospheric trains commence Exeter – Teignmouth.

14 December 1847
Brunel entertains Britain's eleven foremost artists to dinner and commissions a painting from each.

Extends his estate at Watcombe. Lays out the grand design of the park with W.A. Nesfield.

1848
Designs riveted, wrought iron bridge with a 202ft span of box-girder construction for Slough – Windsor branch. Also Wye bridge at Chepstow, a wrought iron, tubular suspension bridge with a 300ft span, plus 300ft iron viaduct. Also 580 yards Landore Viaduct and 400 yards long Newport Viaduct; both timber, both with 100ft central span over rivers.

10 January 1848
Atmospheric traction passenger trains now extended to Newton Abbott.

Hungerford Suspension Bridge, London, c. 1845, thought to have been photographed by W.H. Fox Talbot. Demolished in 1860 to make way for the Charing Cross Railway Bridge. The chains of this bridge were later sold for £5,000 for use on the Clifton Suspension Bridge.
National Museum of Photography, Film & TV

31 May 1848
Newport central span destroyed by fire. Brunel rebuilds with Windsor – type wrought iron span.

19 August 1848
Brunel abandons the atmospheric system.

1848
W.A. Nesfield and James Forsyth employed to assist him in laying out great park at Watcombe.

5 September 1848
WS&WR opened to Westbury.

1 November 1848
B&HR opens Reading – Basingstoke.

1849
Rents villa in Torquay as base whilst working at Watcombe.

May 1849
Work commences on Wye bridge site.

July 1849
Begins to design permanent Paddington station.

8 October 1849
Windsor Bridge opened.

1850
Designing Paddington station. Contributes to the early design for the Great Exhibition building.

1850
Designing timber trestle viaducts for CR and WCR

Crystal Palace Sydenham with one of Brunel's two water towers. The towers survived the fire of 1936 that destroyed the palace but during WWII it was feared they would be landmarks for German bombers and in 1941 they were pulled down.
Crystal Palace Museum

18 June 1850
SWR opens Chepstow – Landore (Swansea).

2 September 1850
GWR opens Oxford – Banbury.

2 October 1850
WS&WR opens Westbury – Frome.

1851
Designing timber trestle viaducts for the Cornish Railway (CR) and West Cornwall Railway (WCR).

February 1851
Brunel undertakes to find contractors for WCR.

February 1851
Awards WCR contract to Ritson & Co.

April 1851
Appointed Chairman of Jury for Civil Engineering, Architecture and Building Contrivances and a Member of the Jury on the Machinery Section for the Great Exhibition.

1 May 1851
Opening of Great Exhibition. Brunel walks alone, fourth from the front of the Grand Opening Procession.

17 – 18 July 1851
OWWR 'Battle of Mickleton Tunnel' (Chipping Campden). Brunel defies the Riot Act. Incites 3,000 men to break the peace.

9 September 1851
WS&WR opens Westbury – Warminster.

19 September 1851
SWR opens Gloucester – Chepstow (East).

March 1852
Brunel resigns as Engineer of OWWR.

25 March 1852
Brunel's first sketch for 'An East India Steamship'. This is the genesis of SS *Great Eastern*.

8 April 1852
Tube for Wye Bridge launched across river and raised.

May 1852
Brunel designs two 12-sided, 284ft high, brick towers carrying 1,200 tons of water for the Crystal Palace – now relocated on Sydenham Hill.

July 1852
Brunel designs a floatable/submersible cylinder 90ft x 37ft and weighing 300 tons, within which the central pillar of the Royal Albert Bridge will be built.

July 1852
Appointed Engineer of Eastern Steam Navigation Company.

14 July 1852
South Wales Railway (SWR), Wye Bridge; one track opened. Through-route from Swansea to Gloucester.

1 October 1852
Brunel travels on the engine of inaugural train Oxford – Birmingham. Crashes at Aynho.

11 October 1852
SWR opens Swansea – Carmarthen.

October 1852
Brunel completes design for the Tamar (Royal Albert) Bridge.

January 1853
Brunel awards contract for construction of Royal Albert Bridge to C.J. Mare.

18 April 1853
Second span of Wye Bridge opened to traffic.

22 December 1853
Brunel and Scott Russell sign contract for design, construction and launch of the 'Great Ship'.

1854 – 1855
Brunel's wire-wound gun barrels tried experimentally by Armstrong, an armaments manufacturer.

1854
Brunel Engineer of Westminster Terminus Railway scheme to cross the Thames and build a station in Victoria St. Scheme never realised.

2 January 1854
SWR opens Carmarthen – Haverfordwest.

16 January 1854
Paddington Station, departure side, opened.

29 May 1854
Paddington Station, arrivals side ,opened. Iron and glass unit construction; very similar to the Crystal Palace Great Exhibition building.

9 June 1854
Paddington Royal Hotel opened. Brunel appointed Chairman of the Hotel Company, though he did not design the building.

1855
Submits a design to the War Office for a semi-submersible gun-ship, steered by underwater jets of steam and carrying a 12in breech-loading gun in a cupola, to bombard Russian Baltic ports.

16 February 1855
Requested by War Office to produce designs for prefabricated, 1,000-bed, portable, hygienic hospital for soldiers wounded in the Crimean War.

24 February 1855
Produces design for the hospital.

138

Liskeard viaduct, before 1894. With a height of 150ft from the valley bottom to the rail, this was the second highest viaduct in Cornwall. *Public Record Office*

7 May 1855
Hospital components unloaded at Renkioi, Dardenelles.

2 June 1855
Hereford, Ross & Gloucester Railway open throughout.

September 1855
Redesigns Scott Russell's paddle boxes on the 'Great Ship'.

September 1855
Redesigns relative height of propeller, resulting in redesign of lower stern.

1856
Construction of the iron trusses of the Royal Albert Bridge, Saltash.

1856
Construction of central column, underwater, of Royal Albert Bridge.

4 February 1856
Scott Russell bankrupted. Work on 'Great Ship' ceases.

15 April 1856
SWR open Haverfordwest – New Milford (Neyland).

23 May 1856
Work re-commences on 'Great Ship'.

June 1856
Brunel orders decks riveted in place on the 'Great Ship' to be re-positioned.

30 June 1856
WS&WR opens Warminster – Salisbury.

1 September 1856
WS&WR opens Frome – Yeovil.

19 September 1856
Scott Russell resigns. Brunel in sole, undivided command of entire shipyard.

20 September 1856
Renkioi Hospital closed and its component parts are auctioned off.

October 1856
Brunel orders (against all advice) fitting of feed–water heating jackets around Great Ship funnels.

November 1856
Central column of Royal Albert Bridge completed to high water level.

1857
Planning the East Bengal Railway.

19 January 1857
Brunel, against advice, plans metal-to-metal runners for 'Great Ship' launching cradles. Awards contract for launch slipway and cradles to Thomas Treadwell.

20 January 1857
WS&WR opens Yeovil – Weymouth.

June 1857
Cornish span of Royal Albert Bridge load-tested.

1 September 1857
Brunel supervises the floating of Cornish span of Royal Albert Bridge into correct position to begin raising span.

3 November 1857
Brunel attempts to launch his 'Great Ship' – now the SS *Great Eastern*. Fails, as predicted.

139

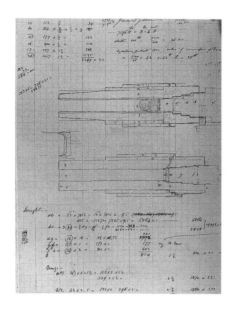

Brunel's sketchbook
design for a floating gun
carriage for the Crimea,
1855.
*University of Bristol
Library*

November 1857 – January 1858
Hydraulic rams force SS *Great Eastern* down 1 in 12
slope on iron-shod cradles.

31 January 1858
3.30am the SS *Great Eastern* finally floats.

February – March 1858
Eastern Steam Navigation Company split on
whether to keep Brunel as Engineer. Advised by
John Fowler to bring back Scott Russell.

March 1858
Brunel remains as Engineer to the Eastern
Steamship Company. Scott Russell returns
as contractor.

May 1858
Brunel and family leave, under doctor's orders,
for Vichy and the Alps.

19 May 1858
Cornish span of the Royal Albert Bridge raised 100 ft
into position. (R.P. Brereton is the Resident
Engineer).

10 July 1858
Devon span of the Royal Albert Bridge floated
into position. (Brunel not able to be present).

September 1858
Brunel returns from Vichy.

25 November 1858
Eastern Steam Navigation Company dissolved.
'Great Ship Company' formed. Brunel is Engineer
and Scott Russell the contractor.

15 December 1858
Brunel ordered to Egypt by his doctor.

30 December 1858
Brunel and family travel up the Nile in an iron
steamboat.

21 January 1859
Brunel and family reach Thebes.

2 February 1859
Ascends cataracts in a wooden boat hauled by 35
labourers. Brunel expresses surprise at their
efficiency.

16 February 1859
Devon span of the Royal Albert Bridge raised into
final position.

2 May 1859
Royal Albert Bridge opened for traffic.

6 May 1859
Brunel and family arrive home.

10 May 1859
Brunel crosses the Royal Albert Bridge on a couch
on a railway wagon.

May – September
Brunel very ill. Visits SS Great Eastern as often as
he can. Work proceeds at a great pace without him.

25 July 1859
Brunel protests at moving of SS *Great Eastern*
engines by Chief Engineer without his permission.

5 August 1859
Banquet on board. Brunel unable to be present.

5 September 1859
Brunel on deck of SS *Great Eastern* collapses shortly
after being photographed.

6 September 1859
Brunel puts his affairs in order. Corrects inventories
of Watcombe Park, orders its sale.

7 September 1859
SS *Great Eastern* steams down Thames.

8 September 1859
6.5pm SS *Great Eastern* is offshore at Dungeness.
Feed-water heating jacket explodes killing many in
the engine room.

9 September 1859
The dying Brunel is told of the explosion.

10 September 1859
SS *Great Eastern* docks at Weymouth.

15 September 1859
Brunel dies in the evening.

20 September 1859
Brunel buried in Kensal Green Cemetery. Funeral
attended by all the engineering establishment,
thousands of railway workers including the
employees of Swindon Works.

20 September 1859
Directors of Cornwall Railway vote to place a
memorial to Brunel on the Royal Albert Bridge:
I.K.BRUNEL. ENGINEER.

1859 – 1860
All the leading civil engineers combine to redesign
and complete Brunel's 1831 suspension bridge over
the Avon Gorge as a funeral memorial to him.

8 December 1864
The Clifton Suspension Bridge opens.

The last photograph –
Brunel by the funnel
of the *Great Eastern*,
5 September 1859.
Seconds later he had
a heart attack.
He died 10 days later.
Brunel University

140

NOTES

4
PADDINGTON
Peter Quartermaine

1 John Gloag, *Victorian Taste: Some Social Aspects of Architecture & Industrial Design from 1820-1900*, David and Charles

2 Michael J. Freeman and Derek H. Aldcroft, *Transport in Victorian Britain*, Manchester University Press 1988

3 J.C. Rolt, *Isambard Kingdom Brunel: A Biography*, Longmans Green, 1957

4 Wolfgang Schivelbusch, *The Railway Journey: The Industrialization of Time and Space in the 19th Century*, The University of California Press, 1986

5 Ibid.

6 J.C. Rolt, *Isambard Kingdom Brunel: A Biography*, Longmans Green, 1957

7 Wolfgang Schivelbusch, *The Railway Journey: The Industrialization of Time and Space in the 19th Century*, The University of California Press, 1986

8 Michael J. Freeman and Derek H. Aldcroft, *Transport in Victorian Britain*, Manchester University Press, 1988

9 Steven Brindle (text) and Richard Bond (plans) *Paddington Station: An Architectural and Historical Survey*, an internal report for English Heritage, London, undated (c.1994) *The Times* for 1 September 1935 quoted a comment by Brunel to the effect that he built Paddington at a low level because he was thus 'able to get a quantity of very good gravel', but also because he felt convinced that 'one day there would be an underground railway running around London at about that level.' Brindle notes that the Metropolitan Railway in London 'was being actively planned from 1852-53.'

8
THE LEVIATHAN
Denis Griffiths

1 Scott Russell's wave line principle was used to determine the ideal shape of the hull in order to reduce the energy loss in making waves. It was one of the first attempts to analyse hull form and its influence upon ship resistance. Scott Russell's theory, however, was incorrect, and it was not until the work of William Froude was published more than a decade later that ship resistance and wave making was put on a true scientific basis.

BIBLIOGRAPHY

1

WORKING FOR THE CHIEF
R.Angus Buchanan

*Once again I express my gratitude to the Archivists of
the Special Collections in the Library of the University of
Bristol for their patience and assistance over many
years of research on the splendid Brunel Collection of
manuscript material:*

Correspondence, (Brunel Collection, University of
Bristol), 1 June 1838 and 20 December 1839

GWR Letter Book 2 (Public Record Office)

Private diary (Brunel Collection, University of Bristol),
26 December 1835

Private Letter Books (Brunel Collection, University of
Bristol) 2A, 2B, 4, 5, 6, 7, 8, 11

R.P. Brereton, 'Centre Pier of Saltash Bridge',
Proceedings of the Institution of Civil Engineers, 1861-
62, 21: pp. 268-276

David Brooke, 'The "Great Commotion" at Mickleton
Tunnel, July 1851', in *Jnl.Rail.& Canal Hist.Soc.*, 1990,
30: 2: pp. 63-67

David Brooke, 'The equity suit of McIntosh v. the Great
Western Railway: the "Jarndyce" of Railway litigation'
in *Journal of Transport History, 1996, 17:2*

David K. Brown, 'William Froude and "the way of a ship
in the midst of the sea"', in R. Angus Buchanan (ed.)
Engineers and Engineering, Bath 1996, pp.179-209

Isambard Brunel, *The Life of Isambard Kingdom Brunel
civil engineer*, Longman Green 1870

R.A.Buchanan, 'The Overseas Projects of I.K. Brunel',
Trans.Newcomen Soc., Presidential Address, 1982-3,
54: pp.145-166

John Cattell and Keith Falconer, *Swindon, Legacy of a
Railway Town*, HMSO for RCHME, 1995

Terry Coleman, *The Railway Navvies*, Penguin, 1968

Ewan Corlett, *The Iron Ship: The History and
Significance of Brunel's 'Great Britain'*, Bradford on
Avon 1974

Daily News, 7 August 1851

Denis Griffiths, Andrew Lambert and Fred Walker,
Brunel's Ships, Chatham, 1999

Brian J.Murless, *Bridgwater Docks and the River
Parrett*, Somerset County Library, 1983

Sir Alfred Pugsley (ed.), *The Works of Isambard
Kingdom Brunel: an engineering appreciation*,
Institution of Civil Engineers, 1976 (in which Angus
Buchanan's contribution on 'I.K.Brunel: Engineer' may
be regarded as an early version of the present essay).

L.T.C.Rolt, *Isambard Kingdom Brunel*, Longman
Green, 1957

James Russell, 'The Newton St. Loe Villa', *Bristol & Avon
Archaeology*, 1992, 9: pp. 2-23

J. Simmons, *The Victorian Railway*, London, 1997

Thomas A.Walker, The Severn Tunnel: Its Construction
and Difficulties 1872-1887, London 1888, reprinted
Bath 1969

R .B.Wilson (ed.), *Sir Daniel Gooch: Memoirs & Diary*,
David & Charles, 1972

3

THE BATTLE OF THE GAUGES
Tim Bryan

Anonymous, *Brunel's Broad Gauge,* The Locomotive,
15 June 1942

Tim Bryan, *Brunel: The Great Engineer*, Ian Allan. 2000

R. B Burdett-Wilson.(Ed), *Sir Daniel Gooch: Memoirs
and Diary*, David & Charles,. 1972

L. Day, Broad *Gauge*, Science Museum, 1985

E.T. McDermot, *History of the Great Western Railway*,
Vol. 1 1927

Rolt. L.T.C, *Isambard Kingdom Brunel*, Longmans
Green, 1957

Adrian Vaughan, *Isambard Kingdom Brunel:
Engineering Knight-Errant*, John Murray, 1991

Various reports and official company documents are
from the collection of STEAM: Museum of the Great
Western Railway, Swindon.

5

A TURKISH PREFAB
Eric Kentley

Derrick Bennett, *Brunel's Britain*, David & Charles, 1985

Isambard Brunel, *The Life of Isambard Kingdom Brunel
Civil Engineer*, Longmans Green, 1870

L.T.C. Rolt, *Isambard Kingdom Brunel*, Longmans
Green, 1957

C. P. Silver, Brunel's Crimean War Hospital – Renkioi
revisted *Journal of Medical Biography*, Volume 6 1998

David Toppin, The British Hospital at Renkioi 1855, *Arup
Journal* 1981, 16 (2): 2 – 18

Adrian Vaughan, *Isambard Kingdom Brunel:
Engineering Knight-Errant*, John Murray, 1991

6

THE FINAL BRIDGE
John Binding

A more detailed account of the Bridge, its design, construction and history to-date is to be found in the author's *Brunel's Royal Albert Bridge*, Truro, Twelveheads Press, 1997.

7

BRUNEL AND THE SCREW PROPELLER
Andrew Lambert

Admiralty Records (Public Record Office, Kew) ADM 92/4

Brunel Collection (Bristol Library) Great Britain Box DM 1758

Brunel's Private Letter Books (University of Bristol Library) 2, 2B and 2C

P. Allington, 'The Sailing Rig of the SS *Great Britain*' *Mariner's Mirror* 1998

J. Bourne. *A Treatise on the Screw Propeller.* London 1855

Isambard Brunel, *Life of Isambard Kingdom Brunel*, civil engineer, Longmans Green 1870

E. Corlett, *The Iron Ship: the story of Brunel's Great Britain.* London 1990

D. Griffith, A. Lambert. & F. Walker, *Brunel's Ships.* Chatham 1999

A. Hylton, *Charles Babbage; Pioneer of the Computer.* Princeton 1982

R. Morriss, *Cockburn and the British Navy in Transition.* Exeter 1998

8

THE LEVIATHAN
Denis Griffiths

Isambard Brunel, *The Life of Isambard Kingdom Brunel*, Longman, 1870

L.T.C. Rolt, *Isambard Kingdom Brunel,* Longmans Green, 1957

Sir Westcott Abel, *The Shipwright's Trade,* Cambridge University Press, 1948

W.S. Lindey, *History of Merchant Shipping and Ancient Commerce*, Sampson, Low, 1876

Sir Alfred Pugsley (ed.) *The Works of Isambard Kingdom Brunel*, Institute of Civil Engineers, 1976

H.P. Spratt, *Marine Engineering*, The Science Museum, London, 1953